2TT 498

28

2TT 498

ENDANGERED
BIRDS

ENDANGERED BIRDS

JAMES FERGUSON-LEES · EMMA FAULL

Foreword by Gerald Durrell

GEORGE
PHILIP

Published in 1992 by George Philip Limited,
59 Grosvenor Street, London W1X 9DA

TITLE PAGE White-naped Crane *Grus vipio*,
one of several cranes now at risk (*see also*
plates 1, 29 and 30).

British Library Cataloguing in Publication Data
Ferguson-Lees, James
  Endangered Birds
  I. Title   II. Faull, Emma
  598

ISBN 0 540 01248 3

Design Louise Dick
Typeset by Keyspools Limited, Golborne, Lancashire
Printed in Hong Kong

CONTENTS

FOREWORD
By Gerald Durrell

Birds are the most enchanting things, colourful musicians who illuminate our lives. Although all animal life is fascinating, birds have a special magic. Hold in your hand a swallow or any other small migrant and you marvel that this thistledown body of fragile bones and sleek feathers can undertake the immense distances it does for its holidays in the sun.

I have had many encounters with birds and all have enriched me. I have watched baby Hoatzins drop from their nest straight into the river, to reappear when apparent danger is over and scramble up through the branches using their feet, beaks and hooks on their wings – making them so like *Archaeopteryx* that it sends a shiver down your spine.

In Patagonia I have seen a conglomeration of a thousand Magellanic Penguin chicks and watched their parents bring food from the sea, crossing huge sand dunes and, with unerring accuracy (ignoring the hundreds of importuning babies), go to their own offspring. I have slept in an eiderdown bed and, awaking, watched a hummingbird like a glittering creature from the hands of Fabergé, brooding and feeding her young in an eggcup-sized nest not a metre from where I lay, thus enjoying different benefits from two species of bird.

Birds are of importance to us, not only as a means of appreciating beauty and as a stimulus to our minds. They grow forests and fruits for us by distributing seeds through their bodies. How could we ever kiss with fervour under the mistletoe if it were not for the gardening of birds? They act as the most gentle, benign and natural of pesticides. One cannot imagine a world without birds – indeed, one would have to be struck deaf and blind. A world without birds would be one in which Man could not live, for they serve us and help us in so many secretive ways.

Sadly, as this book shows, we do not appreciate these gentle inhabitants of the planet as we should. We complain when they remove our milk-bottle tops and sip the cream, or when they make inroads into our strawberry beds or raspberry canes. We, with a selfish savageness, are decimating their world as well as our own. With each tree that is felled there is one less place for a bird to nest, be it a weaverbird's miracle of basketwork or the delicate feather-lined Victorian muff of the Long-tailed Tit.

This is a book that shows what we are doing to the world and how we are affecting the creatures that inhabit the planet with us. Superbly illustrated, it is a plea for beautiful creatures, a plea for their protection and not destruction. It is a plea to save not only them but ourselves, for we are only a strand in the web of life.

PREFACE

We all hope that you will find this book of interest, not least for Emma Faull's beautiful artwork, but it is meant for something more than a brief life on the coffee-table. It is also an overview of bird distribution, and of the problems many species face in different continents. We want it to help sound the alarm.

Some insects attract attention: butterflies for their beauty, flies and mosquitoes for the problems they bring. The fishes of coral reefs provide snorkellers with a wealth of colour. And large mammals, especially in Africa, are most spectacular. But many of the world's more conspicuous and variegated animals are birds, which also produce much of the obvious natural sound.

Birds, too, are often at or near the tops of food-chains. Because of this, and because the numbers of some are relatively easy to assess, they have over the past 40 years become increasingly regarded as indicators of the health of the environment: good and varied populations show that all is well; low numbers or few species signal danger. It is no coincidence that this same period has seen the slow dawning on mankind of the importance of nature conservation.

More than 1000 of the world's bird species are now at best causing concern: over 110 are seriously endangered, dozens more may well be. At least 35 others have become extinct in the twentieth century alone. Many more are at risk at national or local levels.

A world review like this might be tackled in various ways. Grouping threatened birds by habitats, by families and other assemblages of related species, or even by categories of threats, were all discarded here. The problems are too diverse in different continents, and any of these groupings would leave a lot of loose ends. Threats vary greatly in seriousness, but for most the common denominator is Man.

The plants and animals of each of the main continents – additionally separating the temperate north from the tropics and south – tend to form a distinctive complex in what is known as a zoogeographical region. Although many families of, especially, larger birds are common to several, each region is characteristic in those that are or are not represented. Few species and only a third of families are cosmopolitan.

More significantly here, most endangered birds are restricted to one zoogeographical region, so the various chapters attempt to summarise the species at risk in each. The same division was used by my old friend, Guy Mountfort, in his *Rare Birds of the World* (1988): without that as one of several important sources of information (*p.185*), my task would have been much harder.

Nevertheless, our treatment is quite distinct and we hope that the two will be complementary. The birds illustrated are, so far as possible, different and only in a few cases – mainly the plate texts – have I gone into similar detail of individual numbers and conservation measures. Rather have I looked at the broader canvas; and many groups of smaller and more obscure birds have had to be summarised rather than listed individually.

On the other hand, since to consider endangered birds in isolation might leave the reader to think 'How sad' without understanding their significance, I have tried to define the bird families of each region as a background to the species at risk and the threats that face them. Two other sections in each chapter deal with introduced and extinct birds.

Similarly, the texts with Emma's pictures not only include, in many cases, notes on the bird's appearance, habitat and behaviour, and draw attention to the threats to its survival, but aim also to put it against the background of related species. Threatened birds must not be looked at in isolation. What has happened, or is happening, to one can indicate what may happen to others elsewhere.

The Introduction sets the scene and draws together the major threats and problems brought out in the zoogeographical sections. Many people now pay lip-service to the dangers to wildlife, but more must understand the importance of birds as visible indicators of the earth's welfare.

Unless Man contains his reproductive rate, and allows greed to be tempered by sense, the world is destined to become a global zoo in which the individual cages will be national parks and wildlife reserves – some large, most probably all too small – with the remnants of natural habitat managed by governments, charitable bodies, or private enterprise. The rest will be concrete, cultivation and polystyrene theme-parks with wildlife represented by cutouts and video films – all interspersed with blasted war-zones or degraded land leading to desert.

Many animals and plants will have disappeared, unable to cope. There will always be birds, but what are left in the worst areas will often just be the hustlers and the scroungers: House Sparrows and Starlings – or their regional equivalents – and gulls, pigeons, crows and semidomesticated ducks. Few species, signalling danger . . .

James Ferguson-Lees

ACKNOWLEDGEMENTS

The concept of this book was originally nurtured by John Gaisford, publishing director of George Philip Ltd. John's detailed comments on an early draft of chapter 6 helped to shape the content of the rest. Subsequent support and encouragement came from others at George Philip's, especially Jo Hemmings, natural history editor, and Cathy Lowne who put in a great deal of work in the later stages. Earlier, David Christie was responsible for the initial editing and some cutting, and also gave us the benefit of his advice in various ways.

Our single greatest debt, however, is to Dr Nigel Collar of the International Council for Bird Preservation (ICBP): he helped us to decide upon the list of illustrations and, most importantly, read drafts of all the regional chapters and the caption texts. His many comments have made the whole more accurate and up-to-date. But in a few places we did not always accept his suggestions and the final responsibility is, of course, ours alone.

We are grateful to Gerald Durrell for the Foreword; his Jersey Wildlife Preservation Trust is making major contributions in the field of breeding endangered animals, including birds. Iain Bishop and the staff of the British Museum (Natural History) at Tring allowed us access to reference skins and literature, and special thanks for advice and help there are due to Peter Colston, Michael Walters and Effie Warr.

In some ways it was fortunate that the arrival of the galley-proofs coincided with Karen Ferguson-Lees's confinement at home by an unpleasant bout of chicken pox; later, she also spent several evenings helping to check the page-proofs. Others who have assisted in various ways – from commenting on drafts to answering queries, both large and small, and lending books and other material – have included Peter Basterfield, Steve Chatfield, Dr Hilary Fry, Tim Inskipp, Michael King, Andrew Mitchell, David Noakes, Belinda Stewart-Cox, and Gillian Sturgess.

But none of this would have been possible without the now vast published literature of ornithological information. The past 40 years have also seen a slowly increasing awareness of the threats facing our planet and wildlife. This book deals with patterns of bird distributions, and with introductions and extinctions, as a background to the species under threat today. A great many publications have been researched in its preparation: the titles of some are set out in Further Reading (*p.185*) and they, in turn, will give many other references to relevant books and journals.

Ancient origins and modern problems

Apart from major climatic changes – which, of course, continue to have far-reaching effects as they arise – continental drift was the greatest single influence on broad patterns of bird distribution. Around 200 million years ago almost all the world's land was still a single mass, but starting to break up. The evolution of birds from reptiles probably began some 40 million years later, when two supercontinents were drifting apart. These are now known as Laurasia (North America and Eurasia without India and Arabia) and Gondwanaland (all the more southerly lands, including India and a then ice-free and way off-pole Antarctica).

The oldest fossils of true birds are perhaps 130 million years old. The northern continents remained linked for another 50 million years, and Greenland with Europe for even longer. As we have seen (*p.8*), the plants and animals of large sections of each of the main continents form a distinctive complex, whose characters to some extent depend on the length of isolation of that region. The two northern regions – the Nearctic (North America and temperate Mexico) and the Palearctic (Eurasia down to North Africa and the Himalayas) – show affinities, even in their modern birds, and are often taken together as the Holarctic.

The four more southerly continental regions, which also include all the tropics, are the Neotropical (Central and South America and the Caribbean), the Afrotropical (sub-Saharan Africa and south Arabia), the Indomalayan (India to central Indonesia) and the Australasian (including New Guinea, New Zealand, and many adjacent islands). These and Antarctica were still more or less linked 160 million years ago, but then drifted apart more quickly than the northern, especially South America, Australasia and Antarctica. Africa and Arabia stayed joined, as did south-east Asia to the Palearctic, while India moved north past one and then the other to collide with Asia. The Afrotropical and Indomalayan regions have many bird families in common, and affinities with northern Asiatic birds, but the longer isolation of the Neotropical and Australasian is demonstrated by their strikingly different faunas.

Separate identities – and so separate chapters – have also been given here to the Malagasy region (Madagascar and the islands of the western Indian Ocean) and the tropical Pacific islands, as well as Antarctica even though none of its birds is as yet endangered.

The number of bird species in the world today is probably at least 9250. Any exact figure is impossible, because of uncertainty whether some are distinct species or geographical races. Species are groups of interbreeding natural populations that are reproductively isolated from other such groups. But it is difficult to assess whether island or continental populations would have the capability of interbreeding.

Some species will hybridise in captivity, when they would be prevented in the wild by differences in song, behaviour or habitat. Even in the wild, casual interbreeding does not mean that two species are one. It is least infrequent among polygamous birds and those with weak pair-bonds where males play little part in incubation and rearing the young: ducks, which hybridise more than most, are an example.

Interbreeding also tends to occur where numbers are small, so that choice of mates is limited, and a related

THE ZOOGEOGRAPHICAL REGIONS AS ADAPTED FOR THIS BOOK

The major continental faunal regions are those in the Americas (two), Eurasia (two), Africa and Australasia, with transitional zones rather than firm lines where they actually meet. The small Malagasy region, often combined into the Afro-Malagasy, is here extended unnaturally south to the line of the Antarctic Convergence as part of an aim of scooping all oceanic islands into one region or another. But the many archipelagos of the tropical Pacific are treated as an area of their own.

species is becoming commoner and more vigorous. If the rarer has a restricted range, it is in danger of being swamped (*pp.106 and 163*). Hybridisation in general tends to result in infertile eggs and weak embryos or young that may not survive. Progeny that do survive are often sterile. On the other hand, some hybrids are particularly big, strong and aggressive, though usually still with reduced fertility. In conservation terms, it does not matter too much whether we regard an isolated and declining population as a species or a geographical race that may be a species in the making: the important thing is to try to safeguard it.

Taxonomy – the orderly arrangement of living forms – originally relied on external appearance and internal structure, and was largely based on museum specimens. Some similar-looking species proved to be unrelated, their common characters being the result of evolution's adaptation to similar life-modes in comparable habitats. The importance of voice and behaviour in reproductive isolation was realised.

Recently, the genetic information from protein and DNA studies has provided a greater insight into relationships. Indeed, one new species has now been discovered simply through DNA analysis from a single live bird later released (*p.85*). The new world list by Charles G. Sibley & Burt L. Monroe Jr (1990), based on DNA-DNA hybridisation techniques, recognises over 9670 species. It also challenges many of the traditional bird families followed here.

The family is a taxonomic convenience for grouping

related genera. It is interesting, for example, that Sibley & Monroe show the cuckoos and coucals not quite so closely related as previously thought, and the kingfishers and barbets each forming three families. But their list also nearly halves the families of passerines – 'perching birds' and 'songbirds' – from 82 to 46. They have shown relationships not previously understood, but it seems counter-productive to combine all the cuckoo-shrikes, bush-shrikes and monarch-flycatchers with the crows in one vast family of nearly 650; and all the American wood-warblers, tanagers and orioles in an even larger finch family over 990 strong. Even harder to swallow is the placing of the wagtails, pipits and accentors in the sparrow family. It would surely be more useful, while recognising previously unsuspected relationships, to retain smaller families based also on structural and behavioural features.

World totals can, of course, make no allowance for species that have yet to be discovered. Every year one or two new birds are named somewhere in the world, mostly from the tropics; often they have not been found before simply because they are rare with restricted ranges in habitats now increasingly threatened. Many of these new species are thus endangered before their existence is known.

Well over 1000 bird species and distinctive races are causing concern. Each is now given one of several degrees of threat status by the International Council for Bird Preservations (ICBP). Most serious is Endangered ('in danger of extinction ... unlikely to survive if the causal factors continue'). Not far behind are Vulnerable ('less threatened ... but ... likely to move to the Endangered category') and Indeterminate ('Endangered, Vulnerable or at best Rare, but ... not enough evidence to place it definitely'). By Rare is meant that 'the species has a small but stable population which may be at risk ... and requires careful monitoring'. Information is still inadequate for many others of the 1000-plus species but, if the pressures continue, more will be threatened with extinction. During the past century, too, other birds not yet causing concern as species have lost whole populations from parts of their ranges.

It is as well to consider the significance of extinction. During the almost unimaginable length of time since the first birds, huge numbers of species have evolved, flourished and, for one reason or another, disappeared. It has been estimated that, in all, at least 150,000 bird species, perhaps up to half a million, have existed. That would be between 15 and 50 times as many as now, though it is unlikely from the fossil record that the number at any one time has ever exceeded today's figure by more than a thousand or two. There are only so many niches for different species to exploit.

If birds (and other animals) naturally come and go to this extent, does it matter that a tenth or more of today's species are causing concern? Only around 100 are known to have become extinct in the past four centuries of enormous change, so perhaps the threats are exaggerated? Unfortunately, the disappearance of 100 species in 400 years is a far faster rate than anything that may have happened before human beings dominated the planet. And now we have the much greater impact of late-twentieth-century Man with his chemicals, his sophisticated machinery, his obsession with quick profits and, above all, his seemingly unstoppable population growth when many natural controls of disease and early death are being tamed.

Ten thousand years ago the human population totalled only a few millions, no more than today live in Greater London. Already the figure is past 5·5 billions and will have multiplied four-fold in this century alone; some countries are increasing at up to nearly 4 per cent per annum, thus doubling in less than 20 years. Such growth involves the absorption of more and more resources of every kind, from energy to land. Growing human populations and decreasing space also lead to local strife. In such circumstances, nature conservation risks becoming a minor issue again.

In the 1950s and 1960s the greatest threats to wildlife appeared to be from pesticides. The most damaging of these are now banned in North America and much of

Europe, so that major parts of the temperate north are perhaps through the worst of that era, but there are fewer restrictions in some Third World countries; in this connection, it should not be forgotten that hundreds of millions of northern birds migrate south annually to the tropics.

In any event, galloping habitat destruction – for roads and then agriculture, ranching, mining or towns – has become the greatest single scourge of wildlife now. Whether this destruction be of tropical rainforests or British peatbogs, it affects countless forms of animal life that then have to compete for ever-decreasing and often more disturbed remnants of the habitats to which they are adapted.

We live in a world of shortsightedness and greed. Even in Third World countries, there is now an awareness, at least at government level, of the urgent need to safeguard something of our heritage. This principle tends to be accepted if it profits – or at least does not adversely affect – the interests of those concerned. Unfortunately, too, officialdom often has little understanding of the requirements of wildlife. For example, the planting of trees may be seen as an end in itself, without thought of the relative merits of different kinds as habitats, and of the importance of native species over aliens.

Some birds can live with Man in his artificial environments. The success of certain introductions to so many parts of the world is due to the robustness and adaptability of the species concerned. For instance, certain cliff-nesting birds the world over treat tall city buildings as kinds of cliffs. But many species, especially of forests and wetlands, cannot adapt.

Man's persecution takes enormous tolls of birds everywhere. Hunting for food or, on a local scale, for tribal customs may be acceptable; so, arguably, may be shooting for sport if it is legal, if the species is common, and if the methods are fair and humane. But, for example, 'shooting' also includes the chasing of desert and grassland birds and mammals with automatic weapons fired from moving vehicles; and the senseless potting at everything that moves on migration through the Mediterranean.

Trapping for the cagebird trade is no less serious, because it causes prolonged suffering and concentrates on parrots, finches and other families that include many endangered species. Millions of birds are exported from the tropics each year, particularly to Europe, the United States and Japan. Often they travel in appalling conditions, and each live bird that reaches breeders and pet shops represents a little pile of corpses along the way (*p.52*).

Other forms of persecution may be relatively minor on a world scale, but can threaten rarer species, notably birds of prey. The poisoning of carcases, often against foxes or crows, has disastrous results on other scavengers: local populations of vultures, fish-eagles and buzzards have been destroyed. Egg-collecting, not for food but for the generally pointless acquisition of coloured shells for private pleasure, is a seemingly addictive habit that is fortunately largely limited to certain European cultures. On this scale, it has a limited effect, but can present serious problems for rarer species, especially some raptors and others that do not necessarily lay a repeat clutch after the first is stolen. Even falconry has developed its own black market in these days of speedy travel and quick profits: eggs and nestlings are illegally taken to countries where laws and consciences are less strict.

Many more things work against birds. Some, such as oil pollution, affect a wide range of species, particularly seabirds in that case, and – as in recent years in Alaska and the Persian Gulf – can be disastrous on a local scale. Others, which will emerge in the succeeding chapters, may concern just one or two species.

Some birds have tiny distributions, confined to a single archipelago, mountain range or large lake. These are 'endemic' to that restricted locality, and breed naturally nowhere else. Many endangered birds are at risk simply because they are endemic to such areas that are under threat. The endemic birds of small islands are especially vulnerable (*chapters 5 and 8*).

Introductions of alien birds have their greatest effects on islands. Commonly by accident through escapes from captivity, but all too often intentionally, hundreds of bird species have been released in parts of the world where they do not belong. Not far short of 200 are known to have established feral populations. In some places these threaten the very survival of weaker indigenous species. Thus, the section on 'Introductions' under each region is an important part of the general picture.

It is on islands, too, that the great majority of recent extinctions have occurred. The summary of the species lost for ever in each region since 1600, mostly through human activities, is salutary for us all. Although only about 100 birds have gone in those four centuries, the rate is accelerating and the threats greater than ever.

In contrast, a few species and a number of bird families are widespread. Of the 180-odd traditional families, however, fewer than one-third are found naturally in four or more of the six main continental regions. Among these are quite a few seabird groups – such as shearwaters, storm-petrels, cormorants, and gannets. Some seabirds, however, are restricted by latitude. Thus, gulls and terns are on all continents, but gulls are most numerous in temperate zones, and more than half the tern species are tropical; and skuas range over most seas, but nest mainly in the higher latitudes of either hemisphere.

Four-fifths of the petrels and shearwaters, and three-quarters of the albatrosses, breed only in the southern hemisphere, and two-thirds of the storm-petrels in the tropics and northern hemisphere. Tropicbirds and frigatebirds are mainly tropical. Auks are widespread on northern coasts and seas, and replaced ecologically by the unrelated and flightless penguins in the south.

Other waterbirds spend parts of their lives at sea, but for nesting are more associated with fresh water: the circumpolar northern divers, or loons, and two of the three phalaropes, for example. Grebes nest on most

landmasses down to the sizes of Tasmania and the Falklands, but some of them never see the sea. The pelicans are another cosmopolitan family of waterbirds, though, again, most are not marine.

Two of the largest water-associated groups are the waterfowl – ducks, geese and swans – and the waders, or shorebirds. Both are found throughout the world but, again, different kinds are concentrated in different regions. For example, the true geese and many of the diving-ducks, scoters and eiders are largely confined to the northern hemisphere; and, among waders, the great majority of shoreline 'sandpipers' breed in the far north and migrate to and through the tropics. On the other hand, the whistling-ducks, steamer-ducks, stiff-tails and, among waders, jacanas, thick-knees, coursers and pratincoles are mainly tropical and southern, while the dabbling-ducks and the plovers are cosmopolitan.

Two other large worldwide groups are the birds of prey: the half-dozen families of mainly diurnal raptors and the two families of mainly nocturnal owls. Two raptors (Peregrine Falcon and Osprey) and one owl (Common Barn-owl) are the most widespread naturally of all bird species.

Also widely distributed are herons, storks, ibises and spoonbills, partridges and quails, rails, cranes, pigeons, cuckoos, nightjars, swifts, kingfishers, and woodpeckers, as well as, largely in the tropics, parrots and barbets. On the other hand, relatively few families of passerines, have cosmopolitan distributions. The widest-ranging are swallows, pipits, thrushes, crows, and buntings (including American sparrows). One of this last family breeds the farthest north, and another almost the farthest south, of all landbirds.

Most families of small birds tend to be predominantly Old or New World, or not to be found in Australasia. These are discussed separately later as parts of the background to the patterns and problems of the individual regions.

North America and temperate Mexico

The Nearctic ('new northern', from the Greek) includes all of North America, together with north Mexico south to the Tropic of Cancer and an extension down the cooler highlands of the Sierra Madre. It takes in the Aleutians, the Canadian arctic islands, Newfoundland, Bermuda, the Florida Keys, and Guadalupe; but not the Bahamas or, of course, the Hawaiian Islands. Greenland is also excluded here: although geographically part of the Nearctic, its birds, insects and plants – though not its mammals – are closer to those of Eurasia.

However much bigger it may appear on map projections that distort the higher latitudes, North America – third in size of the continents – is only slightly larger than South America. The whole Nearctic is about 21·4 million square km, just 10 per cent bigger than Neotropical Central and South America with the Caribbean islands.

Most of the Nearctic is temperate but, spanning more than 60 degrees of latitude from the edge of the tropics to well north of the Arctic Circle, it has a wide range of climates. Mean temperatures in January and July differ by only 10°C in the south, but by over 20°C for much of the continent and by more than 40°C, even nearly 60°C, in the far north.

The January means around Hudson Bay vary between −20°C and −40°C. Dominated by freezing weather for up to ten months, arctic Canada has temperatures above 0°C only during June–September and just two months frost-free. Even in the cool–temperate zone, south to the Ohio River, winters are long and severe with freezing weather from November to early May. Most birds that nest in the

northern half of North America have to be migratory, travelling down to winter between the southern United States and South America.

The backbone of the Americas is the vast system of mountains down the western side: the Rockies and associated chains to the north extend from Alaska to link with Mexico's Sierra Madre Occidental, and thence through Central America to the Andes. But this is more than just a backbone: the eastern and western cordilleras, with their intermontane plateaux, together dominate much of Alaska, widen to over 1000 km in the United States and, in all, take up some 8 million square km, a third of all of North America. Many peaks exceed 3000 m and four 4000 m; the highest, Alaska's Mount McKinley, is nearly 6200 m. In the east, the far smaller Appalachians – their two highest peaks around 2000 m – extend from Georgia north-east to Pennsylvania, and are represented farther north still by the Laurentian Highlands in Quebec and Labrador.

Below the tundra of Alaska and the Canadian Shield lies a wide belt of boreal coniferous forest. This in turn gives way to the mixed and broadleaved forest that once covered much of eastern North America. In the west, more recently, great tracts of redwood, spruce and other virgin forests of the western United States and, worse, Mexico have fallen to the loggers. The rich central grasslands, or prairies, of the interior from southern Canada southwards are also increasingly damaged by intensive farming. In the south-western United States and north Mexico sizeable sections are subdesert and some true desert.

The smallest of the five Great Lakes covers nearly 20,000 square km (the size of Wales) and the largest,

Lake Superior, is over four times as big. Several other vast fresh waters of Canada exceed 5000 square km, and countless thousands of small lakes and marshes are scattered through the waterlogged tundra and northern forests. In the south, remnant cypress swamps continue to provide important flooded habitats along with, for example, the increasingly threatened sawgrass complex and adjacent mangroves of Florida's Everglades and the river marshes of Louisiana. At just over 6000 km in combined length, the Missouri–Mississippi, flowing out into the Gulf of Mexico, is the fourth longest river in the world.

Indigenous birds

North America holds just over 600 indigenous species of breeding birds, and Nearctic Mexico adds about 120, giving a Nearctic figure of nearly 725. But this is not much more than one-fifth of the number

1
WHOOPING CRANE
Grus americana

*Cranes in general are threatened (see **29**). This one, up to 1.5 m tall, is all white but for black and bare red on the head and black legs and wing-tips. A century ago about 1300 nested in Canada south to Iowa and Illinois, and some in Louisiana, but each year many were shot on migration to and from the Gulf of Mexico. By the 1940s just 15 were left, journeying 6000 km twice yearly between Canada and the Texas coast. Now, with protection and education, there are well over 100; other populations are being established by hatching eggs under the grey Sandhill Cranes. The Whooping Crane's shrill trumpeting, carrying up to 2 km, may yet be more widely heard again.*

2

RAPTOR CAPTIVE-BREEDING,
AND THE CALIFORNIA CONDOR
Gymnogyps californianus

Spanning up to 3 m – almost 10 feet – this and South America's rather differently proportioned Andean Condor are the largest of all raptors. In flight, they are huge, graceful, majestic; perched, like most vultures, they are not pretty. The California Condor's pinkish-yellow head – heavy-jowled, wrinkled, and bare but for sparse black tufts between the red eyes – stands out from a black ruff. The bird is otherwise all black except for whitish legs, a white bar and a grey wash on the upperwings and, in flight, white linings to the underwings.

Taking off with slow stiff beats, California Condors soar and glide on long broad wings slightly raised. Or they used to. Once widespread in western North America, they were confined to California by 1800. By 1940 only 100 were left, and in the early 1970s a mere 50. Shooting, ingestion of lead from animals shot by hunters, poisoning of carcases against eagles and coyotes, egg-collecting and, latterly, pesticides had all contributed. Condors do not breed until at least 6–7 years old; even then a pair raises only one youngster over two years. Adults live long, but repopulation is slow.

In the 1950s the idea of trapping condors for captive-breeding was first mooted, but thwarted in the courts. Thus, it was not until the early 1980s, after a decade in which the annual average of young reared in the wild was only two, that any recovery programme took off. Adults were caught and released with transmitters; eggs were taken for hatching in captivity, leaving the females to re-lay. With protection and public education, the number of wild breeding pairs increased from three to five.

Then in the 1984/85 winter several adults disappeared: one breeding pair and a few single birds remained. The species seemed on the verge of extinction. It was agreed to take the rest into captivity and the last was captured in 1987. By 1990 those held in San Diego and Los Angeles included ten caught when full-grown, four taken as nestlings, 13 hatched in captivity from wild eggs and, most importantly, nine hatched from captive-laid eggs. By late 1991 the total had risen to 52. The ultimate aim is to release at least a hundred California Condors in each of three separate areas of the United States. Meanwhile, to understand the problems, a dozen captive-bred Andean Condors – females only, so that there is no colonisation – have been let out in California since 1988.

Although raptors had first successfully been bred in captivity a century before, the practice was still in its infancy in the early 1950s. Recorded cases worldwide involved fewer than 20 species, several of them only on isolated occasions. There was just one published record of Peregrines, for example, and even by the early 1970s fewer than a dozen young Peregrines had been so reared.

But techniques have advanced enormously in the last two decades: considerable numbers of raptors, especially falcons, are now raised in captivity. The Mauritius Kestrel (**62**) has been saved. Peregrines are being released in various countries to repopulate areas from which they have disappeared. Wild young White-tailed Fish-eagles in Scotland and Griffon Vultures in France have similarly been used for restocking. It seems likely that most birds of prey could be bred or at least reared in captivity. Thus, we are perhaps approaching the time when it will be possible to save any that are in danger of extinction, and falconers will have no excuse for taking raptors from the wild.

3
PIPING PLOVER
Charadrius melodus

Of over 60 plovers worldwide, half are 'ringed' or 'sand' plovers – small, grey-brown and white, mostly with chest-bands or patches at the side. Wings raised on alighting, they run like clockwork, pause with heads up, bob if uneasy, and distinctively tip forward to feed. The Piping Plover – it has a plaintive, melodious, whistled 'peep-lo' – is the palest and rarest of the half-dozen North Americans: sandy-grey above with a black bar on the forecrown, a full or broken chest-band, orange legs and, uniquely, a white rump. It nests on sandy flats from the Prairies eastwards and on Atlantic beaches to the south. Ever more vehicles and dogs on such places are contributing to its decline.

in the Neotropical region (*chapter 2*). Migrants, vagrants and introductions raise the total to over 900.

The indigenous birds belong to some 70 families, nearly two-thirds of which are more or less cosmopolitan. Mainly northern groups shared with Eurasia include the divers, white swans, true geese, grouse, phalaropes and many other waders, and auks, as well as the titmice, treecreepers, nuthatches, kinglets, dippers, and waxwings. These are some of the links between the birds of the northern continents, which were still joined via Greenland and Bering Strait 40–50 million years ago.

More recent links are demonstrated by some migrations. Northern Wheatears clearly colonised North America from both eastern Asia and Europe: the two populations still migrate back in opposite directions to

winter in Africa. Red-throated Pipits, White and Yellow Wagtails, Bluethroats and Arctic Warblers have also established Alaskan footholds from Asia across the Bering Strait.

On the other hand, many Eurasian families are missing. Pheasants and partridges, starlings and true sparrows are in North America purely through introductions. The only larks are the Horned and, very locally, the introduced Sky Lark, as against two dozen in Palearctic Eurasia. The only two wagtails and the one Old World warbler – belonging to a family quite unrelated to the American wood-warblers – are those in the previous paragraph. The babblers are represented in the Nearctic solely by the atypical Wren-tit, and the long-tailed tits just by the aberrant Bushtit. The Wood Stork is the sole stork.

From another direction, some essentially New World families typical of South America have spread

4
ESKIMO CURLEW
Numenius borealis

The curlews are a group of eight shorebirds that breed in North America and Eurasia, and mostly winter well south. All are streaky brown and buff or cinnamon with downcurved bills. Half the size of the largest, at only 30–35 cm, the American Eskimo Curlew has a relatively thin, short and straight beak, and rich cinnamon underparts. Once abundant, it was hunted almost out of existence in the nineteenth century. By the 1920s it was thought extinct, but in the past 30 years occasional migrants have been seen along the Texas coast in spring and farther north in autumn. It is guessed that very small numbers still nest somewhere on the Mackenzie tundra and winter in South America.

5

KIRTLAND'S WARBLER
Dendroica kirtlandii

American warblers are a family quite separate from Old World warblers,
and at least males in summer are mostly much more brightly coloured.
This largish, tail-bobbing, boldly streaked, blue-grey and yellow species
with black face, white eye-marks and two faint wing-bars – the female is
slightly duller – is 'Endangered': adults number fewer than 500. Nesting
only in one part of Michigan, wintering entirely in the Bahamas, and
almost never seen in between, it is dependent for breeding on intensive
management by burning and replanting to maintain stands of jack pines at
8–22 years old with low undergrowth. The parasitic cowbirds that lay eggs in
its nests have also had to be controlled.

over significant portions of North America. Some notable examples of this are the cathartid vultures, hummingbirds, tyrant-flycatchers, mimic-thrushes, gnatcatchers, tanagers, and icterids (American blackbirds and orioles).

Other more tropical families and subfamilies marginally represented in the Nearctic are the darters, or anhingas, the chachalacas (relatives of curassows and guans) and the unique Limpkin, as well as jacanas, skimmers, parrots, trogons, becards, and the Central American silky-flycatchers. Two motmots and two woodcreepers just extend into north Mexico; and the most widespread of the nightjar-like potoos, or 'tree-nighthawks', reaches north to Sinaloa, again just within the Nearctic.

No one bird family is endemic to the Nearctic, though the Wild Turkey is almost restricted to the region, while its sole relative, the rather smaller Ocellated Turkey, lives not much farther south, in Yucatán, Belize and Guatemala.

Nevertheless, certain groups of songbirds are characteristic, with significant numbers of Nearctic species. Sixteen wrens in North America and north Mexico (and nearly 70 in Central and South America) may be compared with one in the whole of the Old World. This family of mostly small, chunky, brown to rufous birds with often cocked tails is represented in the Americas in almost every habitat from desert to marsh, from rainforest to mountain.

All the mimic-thrushes (catbirds, mockingbirds and thrashers), vireos and wood-warblers are confined to the New World, and their distributions suggest that they, like the wrens, may all have been North American in origin, spreading south and there evolving into many further species. The large family of wood-warblers is primarily North American and tropical; most of the vireos are also Nearctic or Caribbean, though often wintering, like the wood-warblers, in Central and South America.

American sparrows belong to the bunting family, but are rather different in appearance and character

6
BACHMAN'S WARBLER
Vermivora bachmanii

Three of 125 warblers in the Americas are classed as 'Endangered', and ten more are causing concern. Bachman's, like Kirtland's (5), has very limited mainland breeding and island wintering ranges, but may already be extinct. Perhaps never numerous, it formerly bred in thickets by old broadleaved swamp-forests in the south-eastern quarter of the United States, and wintered in Cuba. Most of the swamp-forests have gone and so perhaps has much of the winter habitat. If any do still nest, it is likely to be in one vast swamp in South Carolina. The female is olive-green and yellow, with white undertail-coverts; the male also has yellow face and shoulders, and black crown and bib.

from those of the Old World. Over 50 species are found in North America, and a whole lot more in Mexico and Central and South America.

Some 275 species – two-fifths of the indigenous total – are endemic to the Nearctic, but as a whole the avifauna may be regarded as transitional between those of South America and, especially, Eurasia. Indeed, the similarities between the birds of the Nearctic and Palearctic are such that the two are often combined as the Holarctic ('whole northern'). Both are relatively poor in numbers of species and families – well under one-sixth of all bird species live north of the tropics, in what amounts to well over two fifths of the world's habitable landmass (p.60) – but individual birds are often abundant in the far north. For example, North America's higher latitudes provide the main or, often, sole breeding grounds for some 50 species of waders and wildfowl, many in vast numbers.

Introductions

More than 100 species have been introduced into North America, or translocated to other parts of the continent and such islands as Bermuda. Fortunately many have failed, these including Black-bellied Sandgrouse and Dunnock, but at least 25 aliens have become established.

Among them are Mute Swans, mainly in the north-eastern United States; Common Pheasants and half-a-dozen partridges, including Black Francolins in the south-east and Himalayan Snowcocks in Nevada; Feral Rock Pigeons and at least two other doves; half-a-dozen or more parakeets and parrots, all of which have remained local; Sky Larks on Vancouver and San Juan Islands; Red-whiskered Bulbuls; Common Starlings and Crested and Hill Mynahs; House and Eurasian Tree Sparrows; Java Sparrows; and Spot-breasted Orioles in Florida from south Mexico. In addition, House Finches, indigenous in Mexico and the west, have spread rapidly in the eastern states since introduced in the 1940s.

But only six or seven of these naturalised birds are widespread enough to have much impact. The omni-present Feral Pigeon, Common Starling and House Sparrow are all common up to the central latitudes of Canada: Starlings have been killed in millions because of damage to crops and buildings, and their effect on other birds; House Sparrows also cause problems and displace indigenous species from their nests. Less significant are the Common Pheasants and Grey Partridges, the Chukars in the west, and the introduced House Finches in the east.

Some of the rest are largely confined to Florida or the Los Angeles area. In Florida, the Monk Parakeet is a pest of crops and gardens.

Extinctions

The United States leads the world in terms of time, money, research, education and practical work in the field of conservation. In the 500 years since Europeans landed in North America, however, and particularly since the settlements established by the Virginia Company and the Pilgrim Fathers early in the seventeenth century, several bird species have been disposed of and others reduced to dangerous levels.

7
RED-COCKADED WOODPECKER
Picoides borealis

Woodpeckers are missing only from Australasia, Madagascar and oceanic islands. Some adapt well to life with Man. Others need special habitats. Red-cockaded Woodpeckers – pied with barred back and white cheeks, above which males have a barely visible red tuft – bore only into mature pines with diseased heartwood. Although found in pine and pine-oak woods throughout the south-eastern United States, they have decreased everywhere because of forestry practice of removing old and diseased trees. Only 3000 remained by the mid 1980s. The leaving of old trees and woods is now encouraged, with restrictions on pesticide use, and birds are being reintroduced to some former nesting areas.

One extinction is perhaps the most famous of all, apart from the Dodo (*chapter 5*), and remarkable for the numbers that vanished. Passenger Pigeons were longish-tailed doves of eastern North America, the males mainly blue-grey above and rufous-pink shading to white below. Early settlers were quickly struck by their multitudes; many writers between the mid sixteenth and late eighteenth centuries referred to 'clouds' and 'hundreds of millions'. Even allowing for exaggeration, these must have been among the most spectacularly abundant birds ever known. Yet during the nineteenth century they were hunted to the verge of extinction. They had fed and roosted in vast flocks, and nested in the huge colonies which were apparently necessary for successful breeding and defence against predators. As the numbers dropped, the decline snowballed. The last one died in captivity in 1914.

Less familiar and less spectacular, but comparable in timing and area, was the extinction of the Carolina Parakeet, the only parrot indigenous to North America. Green with some orange about the otherwise yellow head, it showed yellow also on the shoulders and thighs. Carolina Parakeets were persistently persecuted as pests of fruits and cereals. They used to appear in flocks of 200 or more; hundreds could be killed in a day, and as many as 20 with a single shot. Perhaps also affected by habitat destruction, they decreased rapidly in the early nineteenth century. Again, it was probably 1914 that saw the end.

Two specialities of Guadalupe Island 250 km off the coast of Baja California (not to be confused with the West Indian Guadeloupe) are known, or in one case believed, to have gone early this century. These were the Guadalupe Caracara (last recorded 1900) and the Guadalupe Storm-petrel (1912), though the latter's loss is not conclusive. Caracaras, confined as a family to the Americas, are scavenging birds of prey related to the falcons; the one on Guadalupe – wiped out by a temporary population of Angora goatherds – has the dubious distinction of being the world's only diurnal raptor to have become extinct in the last 400 years.

The essentially marine Labrador Duck (1875), the flightless Great Auk (about 1800) – which hung on later in Scotland and Iceland (*p.67*) – and, if it was a distinct species, Townsend's Finch (1833), a relative of the American Dickcissel, are the only other definite extinctions of Nearctic birds since 1600. But Bachman's Warbler (*see* **6**) may now be extinct and the mainland race of the Ivory-billed Woodpecker has almost certainly gone, leaving Cuba as its only hope (*p.50*).

Threatened birds

Although there are worries at local levels, the number of Nearctic birds which are currently causing concern as species is less than two dozen, at 4 per cent a small proportion of the total compared with some other regions. Eight are classed as 'Endangered', and three as 'Vulnerable'.

Three species are the subject of special captive-breeding programmes. Some success has been achieved by placing eggs laid by captive Whooping Cranes (**1**) in the nests of wild Sandhill Cranes. All California Condors (**2**) are now in captivity, but it is hoped soon to release a number back to the wild.

8

IMPERIAL WOODPECKER
Campephilus imperialis

Up to 60 cm long, this largest of the world's 200 woodpeckers is seven times the size of the smallest. Or it may already be a matter of 'was': none has been recorded since 1958 except, just possibly, in 1977. (Likewise, the similar but smaller Ivory-billed has not been reliably reported in the United States since the 1950s.) All black but for white 'braces' and wing-patches, and the male's red crest – the female's is black and more strongly upcurled – the Imperial was once widespread in Mexican pine forests above 2000 m. But it needed mature trees and seclusion. Numbers decreased rapidly through logging and, especially, shooting as forests were opened to roads and settlements.

The third captive-breeding project involves the Peregrine Falcon, a cosmopolitan bird which is not at risk as a species, but is particularly susceptible to the build-up of pesticides in the environment and thus in the pigeons and other birds that are its main prey. Peregrines declined in much of the northern hemisphere from the 1950s on. By the late 1970s, North America south of the tundra had only a few hundred pairs left, all but 150 of them on the Aleutians and the coasts of Alaska and British Columbia: the North American race had been brought close to extinction. The paler tundra race, although reduced to perhaps half its numbers of 30 years earlier, still mustered a few thousands, but this is a migratory form that winters down to South America. More recently, it too has declined, perhaps through ingestion of pesticides in its winter quarters.

The next three threatened species are all migrant waders, or shorebirds, with very different problems. The little Piping Plover (3), increasingly threatened by Man's leisure activities on the sandflats where it nests, is currently declining. In contrast, the Eskimo Curlew (4), long at rock bottom and classed as 'Endangered', was the victim of enormous shooting pressure in the nineteenth century and at one time was thought extinct; it hangs on in minute numbers.

The somewhat bigger Bristle-thighed Curlew, Whimbrel-sized and with a similar head-pattern, breeds in westernmost Alaska and winters on Pacific islands. The first recorded nest was not found until 1948 and, though the population was put at 7000 in 1991, the fact that the breeding range is limited to two core areas puts it at some risk; as a transoceanic migrant, too, it faces other dangers. Winter flocks of up to 100 individuals or more occur in the north-western Hawaiian Islands and elsewhere in Polynesia and Micronesia; in some places they live largely on a diet of seabird eggs.

Two other migrants classed as 'Endangered' are Kirtland's (5) and Bachman's Warblers (6), both of which have very precise habitats and tiny breeding and wintering ranges. Two more southerly American wood-warblers – the Golden-cheeked of central Texas, which winters in Central America between Mexico and Nicaragua, and the sedentary Altamira Yellow-throat of north-east Mexico – are also uncommon with very limited ranges, but their status and any problems are insufficiently known.

Apart from the very remote possibility of the Ivory-billed Woodpecker that is now almost certainly extinct there, the only other threatened landbirds of the United States are two that breed in the south-east – the migratory Black-capped Vireo, which winters in north-west Mexico, and the sedentary Red-cockaded Wood-pecker (7). The Black-capped Vireo is the smallest and one of the most attractive of the dozen vireos found in North America. All look superficially like American wood-warblers, but have relatively short thick bills; most eat fruits as well as insects. This one is olive and white, with yellow flanks and either a glossy black head and white spectacles (male) or a dark grey head (female). It used to be regarded as fairly common in oak scrub and thickets in western Oklahoma, central Texas and north Mexico, but is now apparently much scarcer.

The Ivory-billed Woodpecker – formerly found between South Carolina and Texas, in mature river forest and old cypress swamps with a leavening of dead trees – was probably never common and many were shot by collectors around the turn of the century. More serious were the gradual drainage and clearance of much of its habitat. By 1939 only two dozen of these large woodpeckers were left; the last confirmed records were in the 1950s, since when most of the occasional reports refer to the somewhat smaller and not uncommon Pileated Woodpecker. A few protected areas of suitable swamp-forest are still left in Florida and Texas but, if any Ivory-bills remain, there can hardly be enough to maintain a viable population. The Ivory-billed is very like Mexico's Imperial Woodpecker (8), though smaller, with rather less white on the wings, and with the white 'braces' extending up the sides of the neck. The Imperial, classed as 'Endangered', may similarly already be extinct.

The north Mexican part of the region also accounts for the remaining six Nearctic landbirds at risk, and most of the seabirds. The smallest and most inconspicuous is the Sierra Madre Sparrow, rare throughout its patchy range in the bunch-grass areas of the mountain pinewoods of western Mexico. The other landbirds are representatives of essentially tropical families or groups – a trogon, a wood-partridge and three parrots.

The Eared Trogon (**9**) is one of the two most northerly trogons; and the rare Bearded Treequail, confined to pine forest with grassy ground cover around the 1500-m mark in the Sierra Madre Oriental, is the northernmost of three small but longish-tailed highland partridges of Central America.

The Thick-billed Parrot (**10**), of the Sierra Madre Occidental, is 'Vulnerable'. Its close relative in the Sierra Madre Oriental, the Maroon-fronted, was classed as 'Endangered', but the population is now considered stable. Sometimes treated as conspecific, these two, also known as 'macawlets', are extremely

similar but for the colour of the forehead. The adverse factors – logging and other deforestation, disturbance and trapping – are much the same for both, but, whereas the Thick-billed nests in tree cavities (and so suffers more from selective felling of old timber), the Maroon-fronted breeds in cliffs.

The third parrot that may be at risk – on the grounds of limited range, deforestation and, in particular,

9
EARED TROGON
Euptilotis neoxenus

*Solitary, arboreal and insectivorous (some also eat fruits), trogons have stubby bills and longish square-cut tails. Most are tropical (see **21**), but three live in temperate Mexico: the Elegant in dry woods (also into Arizona), the Mexican in cloud forest, and the Eared. Thickset, angular-rumped and small-headed (ear-tufts very obscure), the last is limited to Mexican pine-oak forests above 2000 m. Scarce in a small range, it must be at risk from logging. But, while glossy greens and blues, red abdomen and broadly white-tipped undertail (usually closed) may look eyecatching, trogons perch unobtrusively and numbers are hard to assess. The duller female has head and chest grey.*

trapping – is the smaller Red-crowned Amazon from the temperate parts of four states of north-east Mexico. In its case not enough is known about the size of the population to be sure of the extent to which it is under threat. Ironically, the species has some security in feral populations established by escaped cagebirds around Miami and Los Angeles.

This almost completes the story for north-temperate America, except for a few rare or local seabirds in the south of the region, mostly nesting on small islands. All but one are from the Pacific side. Two almost wholly blackish storm-petrels – the tiny Least and the much larger Black – nest on various islands off Baja California and the latter also on Santa Barbara Island, California. Both are still in good numbers, but their breeding ranges are very limited and, as stressed elsewhere, unprotected island populations are open to many problems. The Black-vented Shearwater also nests on islands off Baja California, and is threatened by cats and rats. Its close relative, Townsend's Shearwater – both are often treated as races of the Manx Shearwater – is similarly at risk on Socorro and other islands of the Revillagigedo group more than 1000 km farther south (*chapter 2*).

Finally, on the Atlantic side and classed as 'Endangered', the Bermuda Petrel – known also, onomatopoeically from its voice, as the Cahow – is something of an epic. It used to nest in vast numbers when Bermuda was discovered in the early 1500s, but introduced pigs and rats caused a decline which the early settlers all but completed by eating the nesting birds. For nearly 300 years from the mid seventeenth century the species was thought extinct until, after the identification of odd corpses in the first half of the twentieth century, nests were found on offshore islets in 1951. Ever since, the tiny colony has been nurtured through hazards ranging from pesticide contamination to the depredations of tropicbirds: there is room for thousands, but the population on five islets is still probably under 100. This species is closely related to the West Indian Black-capped Petrel, itself so reduced as to be 'Vulnerable' (*chapter 2*).

10
THICK-BILLED PARROT
Rhynchopsitta pachyrhyncha

Most parrots are tropical, but some extend into southern temperate regions and a few are found farther north. Apart from the extinct Carolina Parakeet (p.26), and escaped species now breeding ferally in England and Florida, the northern limits are Afghanistan and Mexico. Mexican forest parrots are under serious threat from logging and, with consequent improved access, from trapping for the cagebird trade (23). The large Thick-billed – green with red forehead, eyebrows, shoulders and thighs, and a yellow band on the underwings in flight – is now increasingly rare in its natural pine-oak forests of north-west Mexico over 1500 m, so is being introduced to comparable habitat in Arizona.

Central and South America and the Caribbean

For birds, this is by far the richest region: no other can boast much more than half as many species. Upwards of 40 per cent of all bird species use the land or its inshore seas for breeding or as migrants during the northern and antarctic winters.

The name 'Neotropical' ('of new tropics') applies to tropical Mexico, the Caribbean islands (including the Bahamas just north of the Tropic of Cancer) and all of Central and South America. The northern boundary loops through west-central Mexico, taking in the tropical lowlands but not the more temperate uplands of the Sierra Madre north of 20°N. All islands are included as far as the Revillagigedos, Galápagos and Juan Fernández in the eastern Pacific, and Fernando de Noronha, Trindade (not to be confused with Trinidad) and the Falklands in the western Atlantic.

Thus, the region is mostly tropical but spans over 80 degrees of latitude down to the southern equivalent of Edinburgh or central Labrador. There the mean July (midwinter) temperatures are 5–10°C, compared with 15–20°C in January (midsummer). It may seem surprising to include a southern cool-temperate zone in a tropical region, but many of the landbirds of the bottom third of South America represent southward extensions by tropical families. Winter temperatures are nothing like as low as in northern North America and Eurasia: summer and winter means differ by only a half to a third of the corresponding figure in the far north. In southern South America, therefore, seasonal migrations are of far smaller significance.

At 17·6 million square km, South America is only the fourth largest of the continents, but two-thirds as big again as Europe and over twice the size of Australia. The inclusion of Central America and all the islands takes the total to 19·4 million square km, making this also the fourth in size of the zoogeographical regions.

South America has the world's longest mountain range, the Andes, curving 8500 km down its western side, with a maximum width of 700 km and eight peaks over 6000 m. The northern Andes grade from humid subtropical to cold mountain forest below a band of upland steppe that reaches to the snowline; even in tropical Colombia and Ecuador the night temperature here may drop to −2°C. Farther south the mountain steppe is known as 'puna'. A band of mixed beech forest extends along the lower southern Andes.

The continent also has the world's greatest river, the Amazon, totalling 6500 km, and – now under such threat – the richest and most extensive rainforests. The Amazon basin's drainage area of some 7 million square km is ten times the size of Texas; the forest itself used to cover over 5 million square km, ten times the size of France, but is being steadily whittled away.

To the north of the Amazon basin and east of the Andes lie the savannah grassland *llanos* of central Venezuela. East of the Orinoco, these give way to the rounded hills and narrow valleys of the Guiana Highlands, rising to 2–3000 m; here the Angel Falls, narrow but the world's highest, have a drop of 980 m. Along Venezuela's southern border with Brazil lie the *tepuis*, groups of plateaux with mixed savannah and deciduous forest in a climate that varies seasonally from very wet to arid.

South of the Amazon, the great Brazilian tableland includes dry forest, savannah and scrub from the Mato Grosso eastwards, as well as the often remnant pine,

11
BLACK-FRONTED PIPING-GUAN
Pipile jacutinga

The 45–50 curassows, guans and chachalacas are arboreal turkey-like birds with stubby decurved bills, rounded wings, and longish tails and legs. Mainly in tropical American forests, they eat shoots and fruits, running along branches or jumping from one to another; most build twig nests in trees. Half-a-dozen that have limited ranges in extensively deforested areas are now classed as 'Endangered'. Some 60 cm long, and glossy violet-blue-black with white crest and shoulders, white streaks below, bare red dewlap, and red legs, this is the rarest of the three called piping-guans. Once common in south Brazil and adjacent Paraguay and Argentina, it has been hunted to excess in decreasing habitat.

12
HORNED GUAN
Oreophasis derbianus

Half as big again as the piping-guans (11), this rare bird is almost the size of a hen turkey. Glossy green-black, with a white tail-band and finely streaked white breast, it also has a yellowish bill, white eyes, and red lower throat and legs. The name refers to the thin red bony projection on the crown. Its call is a far-carrying mooing or booming 'oo-oo-oo' of 3–4 notes. Like the bigger curassows, it spends much time on the ground, but is equally at home in trees. This is another of the half-dozen endangered curassows and guans (ten more may also be at risk): deforestation and hunting have confined it to a few forested volcanic peaks over 2500 m on the Guatemala–Mexico border.

mixed deciduous, subtropical and tropical forests of intervening lower ground and of the Brazilian Highlands towards the south-east. On one of the tributaries of the Paraná, South America's second greatest river, the Falls of Iguazú are second only in height and length combined to Africa's Victoria Falls. Farther west, in an enclave into the Brazilian plateau along the border with Bolivia, the low-lying plains, rivers and marshes of the *pantanals* flood seasonally into a huge swamp.

In turn, these features give way to the dry scrub woodland of the *chaco* of Paraguay and north Argentina, the luxuriant grassland *pampas* of east-central Argentina – now largely cultivated and grazed – and, farther south, the vast steppes and semidesert of Patagonia. Much of South America is low-lying.

Most Neotropical lakes are relatively small – only Lago Titicaca, 200 km long on the Andean borders of Peru and Bolivia, and Lago de Nicaragua, also over 8000 square km, come into the world's top 30 – but small sheets of fresh water are abundant in, for example, the vast open flats of east-central Argentina. Apart from the coastal zone between south Ecuador and north Chile, the Neotropical region also has less

true desert than other continents; the so-called desert of Patagonia is largely covered with prickly scrub. The more northerly coasts still have extensive mangroves, but these are under pressure.

In Central America, comparable but lower mountains, humid and dry forests, savannahs and subdesert have to jostle in relatively small areas.

Cuba, south of Florida, and the arc of the West Indies down to eastern Venezuela, are the summits of submerged mountains. As such, most have rugged hills and mountains more or less covered with greenery, though much of that is secondary growth. Cuba itself is not much smaller than either Florida or England, and the total area of the Caribbean islands amounts to nearly a quarter-million square km. The highest peak, in the Dominican Republic, is well over 3000 m.

Indigenous birds

The Neotropical region can boast some 3425 indigenous species of breeding birds. South America alone has about 2680; Central America throws in a further 550; and some 175 endemics are added by the relevant island groups, especially in the Caribbean where a few more northern species also just encroach. The inclusion of migrants that spend the northern and antarctic winters in the Neotropics means that nearly two-fifths of all bird species use just one-eighth of the landmass and its inshore waters.

Diverse areas of a few square kilometres in Colombia, Ecuador or Peru may hold well over 500 species; a comparable piece of tropical Africa or Asia is unlikely to exceed 300–350. Colombia boasts a national list of almost 1700 species, more than any other country anywhere. Even Argentina's 950 compares favourably with, say, Australia's 730, especially as Argentina is only about one-third the size and, in contrast, hardly extends into the tropics.

In all, just over 100 families of birds breed in the Neotropics, but four are introduced (*p.41*) and six are Nearctic elements that just reach into the extreme north. These latter are the cranes (the Sandhill nests

13
KEEL-BILLED MOTMOT
Electron carinatum

Related to kingfishers and, like many of them, nesting in burrows dug into banks, the essentially tropical motmots are characteristic of Central America. Most are 30–50 cm long with longish, broad, slightly downcurved bills, and long graduated tails swinging like pendulums: the elongated central feathers grow fully vaned, but loose barbs fall to leave racket tips. They perch motionless, low in streamside forest, darting out to pick insects, frogs or fruits from tree, ground or air. Found in the Caribbean foothills from south Mexico to Costa Rica, this is the rarest of the nine. Green with rufous forehead, blue eyebrows, and black mask and breast-spot, it has a loud chicken-like cackle.

14

BLACK-HOODED ANTWREN

Myrmotherula erythronotos

Many of the huge tropical American family of antbirds will – some regularly – follow army ants on the march through the forest; they seldom eat ants, but dart in for other insects, spiders, frogs and lizards disturbed by these processions. Antbirds come in various shapes and sizes, as reflected by such names as antshrikes, antpittas, antthrushes, antvireos and antwrens: the largest antshrike is four times as big as this antwren which, only 9 cm long is an endangered forest bird rediscovered in south-east Brazil in 1987. Head, breast, tail and white-marked wings are slate-black on the male, olive-brown on the female; both have rufous backs, he a grey belly and she a buff.

only in Cuba), the shrikes (south Mexico) and the essentially northern families of tits, long-tailed tits, nuthatches and treecreepers which all have one or more representatives down to south Mexico or even slightly farther.

Three other families occur only as winter visitors: auks and waxwings in the extreme north and sheathbills in the far south. Ospreys, too, are purely winter visitors, except in the Bahamas and on some cays off Cuba and Belize.

Among cosmopolitan groups, ibises, wildfowl, raptors, and pigeons are particularly abundant, some in huge numbers, and, among tropical forest families, parrots, trogons and barbets. While North America has no flamingos, the South is the only continent with three. Shared with the Nearctic are one darter, or anhinga, and one skimmer. As in the other two main tropical regions, the finfoots, or sungrebes, are also represented by a single species.

On the other hand, apart from the Central American turkeys, the only galliform birds are a high proportion of the 30-odd American quails, these mostly in Central and northern South America; there are few kingfishers; and, though the West Indies have four black crows, the only crows south of Nicaragua are more than two dozen brightly coloured jays.

Many seabirds occur offshore as non-breeding visitors; quite a few also nest. The latter include seven penguins, the most northerly in the Galápagos; two albatrosses, in the Galápagos and Falklands; and over 25 shearwaters, petrels, storm-petrels and diving-petrels, mainly on islands.

What makes the Neotropical avifauna so different is that, of the 90-odd characteristic families, almost one-third – a very high proportion – are endemic or, in half-a-dozen cases, virtually restricted to the region but for a few species that reach into Nearctic Mexico or the southern United States. Some of these are among the most numerous and diverse of all bird families: the evolution of four into two or three hundred species each has filled every niche.

First, however, among the less numerous endemic families are the three rheas (equivalents of ostriches and emus in other southern regions); the 46 tinamous (unrelated to the partridges that they replace and superficially resemble); the three screamers (noisy, bulky, goose-like); the three trumpeters (gregarious forest-dwellers like small rheas); the two seriemas (bustard-like, with shaggy hawkish heads and long tails); and the four seedsnipes (which appear dove-like but are actually waders).

Others are the five potoos (tree-nightjars, the New World equivalents of frogmouths); the nine motmots (see **13**) and five West Indian todies (both reminiscent of kingfishers); the 13 American barbets (see **22**) and, now known to be related, the 42 huge-beaked toucans; and the 17 long-billed jacamars and 33 large-headed puffbirds (related but respectively more reminiscent of busy bee-eaters and sluggish shrikes).

The rare Magellanic Plover is hardly a typical plover and arguably better placed in a family of its own: endemic to southernmost Argentina and Chile, it has the proportions of a small grey and white Turnstone, but its gait, feeding behaviour, and habit of regurgitating food to its young are all remarkable. Each of three other single-species families is reminiscent of two very different ones: the Hoatzin, a sort of leaf-eating pheasant-guan of riversides, with tiny head and untidy bristly crest; the Sunbittern, a heron-rail with long neck and tail; and the Oilbird, a hawk-nightjar colonial in caves, that feeds nocturnally on fruit.

The wailing Limpkin, again the only species in its family, nests from Argentina to Florida and Cuba, but is primarily Neotropical. Almost all the curassows and guans (see **11–12**) are also South and Central American; the same applies to the caracaras and the Neotropical falcons. Also Neotropical are over half the cathartid vultures, now known to be more closely related to the storks than to the other birds of prey.

Small landbirds are particularly well represented in the Neotropics and account for over two-thirds of the total of 3050 endemic species. The huge family of hummingbirds (see **16–17**) extends to Alaska, but some 310 of the 330 are confined to South and Central America, the Caribbean and other islands. Equally characteristic are ten essentially New World passerine families that together total 1050 species.

One of the largest involves the ovenbirds – no relation of the American wood-warbler of that name – and the spinetails: a diverse and evocatively named collection of earthcreepers, streamcreepers and palm-creepers; brushrunners, treehunters and reedhunters; leafscrapers and foliage-gleaners; wiretails, thistletails, prickletails and softtails; and plushcrowns, tufted-cheeks, hookbills and recurvebills; as well as thorn-birds, miners, cachalotes, canasteros and cinclodes.

Most are small, a few up to 25 cm; some are short-tailed, others longer. Nearly all are insectivorous. Many are terrestrial: most walk rather than hop; others prefer running to flying; many skulk unobtrusively. The 220 species have adapted to fill many niches, from garden, field and swamp to forest, upland steppe and mountain. The cinclodes, for example, take the place of dippers on torrents; the recurvebills or treehunters and the treerunners help to fill the tree-creeper and nuthatch niches; foliage-gleaners hunt the canopy like warblers.

Some of the ovenbirds make conspicuous 'Dutch ovens' of mud. The spinetails and thornbirds build large, impenetrable stick nests, epitomised by the Firewood-gatherer's untidy heaps on telegraph poles. Many more nest in holes in trees or banks, and the miners excavate their own. All this family shares dull colours (browns and rufous above, paler or whiter below, though some have bright patches) and harsh voices with poor or non-existent songs.

On the other hand, several of the related family of woodcreepers – at least 50 species of spiny-tailed rufous-brown and buff tree-climbers that hunt and feed like huge treecreepers – produce quite musical notes and trills.

Two even more numerous families are the antbirds (see **14**), with nearly 240 species, and the tyrant-flycatchers, with over 380. The latter replace the Old World flycatchers in the Americas; some also fill the niches of warblers, pipits, wrens, thrushes, shrikes, and jays. Nearly three dozen tyrants breed in North America, but ten times as many in the Neotropics. Some are unobtrusive, others very conspicuous.

Varying greatly in size, from 5 to 28 cm, many of the tyrants are soberly dressed in olive-browns, browns, greys or blacks with whitish to yellow underparts. But some have striped heads and are bright yellow below, a number have a partly hidden red, yellow or white crown-streak, two are mainly white, several largely black, and one each red and multicoloured.

Like so many Neotropical landbirds, the tyrants are poor songsters. Most produce no more than whistles or short trills, though these are often loud and form a good part of the 'dawn chorus'. Some of the forest antbirds give attractive little warbles but, again, most of them have nothing more than simple whistles or melodious chatters.

The same applies to the other half-dozen endemic families. Apart from the unique Sharpbill – an aberrant tyrant, but heavily black-spotted below – these are the compact and neckless, but long-legged, terrestrial gnateaters; the long-legged, tail-cocking and equally terrestrial tapaculos; the highly variable cotingas (see 15), which tend to have loud calls and elaborate displays; the acrobatic and often colourful manakins, many of which produce mechanical sounds and also have elaborate displays; and the superficially finch-like plantcutters, which can manage no more than rasping croaks and rattles. Most, except the last, are primarily birds of forest or dense cover.

Many of the true songbirds of the region belong to families shared with North America or even the Old World. Among the latter are swallows, pipits, dippers, wrens, thrushes and finches, together with the Horned Lark which has isolated populations in south Mexico and the east Colombian Andes. The wrens really belong to the New World, although one is widespread in Eurasia: the Americas have nearly 70 different

wrens, of which the North has nine, Mexico 27, and Central and South America over 50. The buntings known as 'sparrows' in the Americas are also an essentially New World group.

Strictly American songbird families shared between North and South include the mimic-thrushes (mockingbirds, thrashers and catbirds), vireos, wood-warblers, tanagers (see 18), and icterids (American orioles, blackbirds, meadowlarks and cowbirds).

Central America's avifauna is far more typical of South than of North America, but south Mexico is somewhat transitional. It has its own endemic species from South American groups, but other Neotropical families are lacking. Instead, additional Nearctic families are marginally represented (pp. 35–6).

The West Indies, being islands, have a relatively limited avifauna that is also transitional between the two regions. But there are about 150 endemic species. Half-a-dozen of these belong to two endemic families. The five insectivorous todies are small and dumpy, iridescent green above, with red bills and crimson throats; related to motmots and kingfishers, they also excavate nest-burrows. The unique Palmchat,

15

LONG-WATTLED UMBRELLABIRD
Cephalopterus penduliger

The three umbrellabirds – crow-sized, blue-black, with silky hair-like 'umbrella' crests – are the largest of the cotingas, a tropical American group of over 60 diverse but chiefly fruit-eating forest birds. One, the Bare-necked, has an inflatable scarlet throat-pouch; the other two a feathered wattle that, on this male Long-wattled, can stretch to 35 cm. He advertises by jumping from branch to branch with a booming grunt, crest and wattle spread; but in flight the crest is laid back, and the wattle shortened and pulled up. Confined to humid lower slopes of the Andes in west Ecuador and Colombia, this species suffers from deforestation, hunting and, not least, cagebird trappers.

confined to Hispaniola, is closest to the northern waxwings: grey-brown to greenish above and white below with dark stripes, it is remarkable for building communal nests in which each of a number of pairs has its own chamber and entrance.

Other West Indian landbird families with one or more endemic species include pigeons, parrots, owls, cuckoos, nightjars, swifts, hummingbirds, trogons, woodpeckers, tyrant-flycatchers, swallows, wrens, mimic-thrushes, thrushes, gnatcatchers, crows, vireos, finches, wood-warblers, tanagers and honeycreepers, buntings, and icterids.

Jamaica alone has nearly two dozen endemics, as does Cuba where about half are causing some concern. One such, the scarce Bee Hummingbird, is the smallest bird in the world, just 6 cm long (including its bill), often weighing less than 2 g (one-fourteenth of an ounce) and, as its name suggests, as likely to be mistaken for a bee as a bird; the blue-green and whitish male has a brilliant red head and throat-plumes.

Island groups elsewhere in the region have their own endemics, of which the most famed are the 13 Darwin's finches on Galápagos and one more on Isla del Coco half way to Costa Rica. Like the Hawaiian honey-creepers (*chapter 8*), these are supposed to have evolved from a single colonisation by an ancestral finch. Endemics on the Islas Juan Fernández include a buzzard, a hummingbird (*see* **16**), a spinetail and a tyrant-flycatcher; and on the Revillagigedos a wren and a mockingbird, as well as several distinctive races of mainland species. The Falklands have only one endemic, a steamer-duck, but add two or three penguins to the breeding list.

Large numbers of birds that are partly or entirely summer visitors to North America spend the northern winters in the Neotropics. These range from such passerines as tyrant-flycatchers, swallows, vireos, wood-warblers, tanagers and certain icterids, to storks, ducks, raptors, terns, cuckoos, nightjars, swifts and, especially, waders. Argentine concentrations of thousands of Wilson's Phalaropes are spectacular.

16
JUAN FERNÁNDEZ FIRECROWN
Sephanoides fernandensis

Hummingbirds live in the Americas from Alaska to Tierra del Fuego, but mainly in the tropics; there they use most habitats from garden and forest to semidesert, and from sea-level to the snowline. This one used to be common on Chile's Juan Fernández islands, but now a mere 400–800 remain, all on Isla Robinson Crusoe. Its decline is not due to any serious competition from the related and commoner Green-backed Firecrown (found in Chile and Argentina too), but rather because it now lives in introduced vegetation where introduced rats and coatis prey on its nests. The male is brown-red with an iridescent ruby crown, the female turquoise-green above and more green-spangled below.

Introductions

Over much of the region, relatively few introduced birds have been established and most are very local. Only Feral Pigeons and House Sparrows are widespread: even they are patchy, mainly in Mexico and Guatemala, on Caribbean islands, and in southern South America north to Peru and south Brazil. House Sparrows were brought to Argentina in the 1870s to control insects, but are now themselves considered pests that damage grain and fruit, contaminate food, distribute parasites, and displace indigenous species from their nests.

Other aliens in South America are mainly small birds – perhaps originally escapes – such as European Greenfinches (currently spreading) and Goldfinches, and Common Waxbills, mostly in north-east Argentina, Uruguay or eastern Brazil. A few South American species, even hummingbirds, have also been translocated within the continent, and some to Panama and Costa Rica.

California Quails have been established locally in Chile and Argentina, but attempts at introducing bobwhites in South America, and Common Pheasants anywhere, have failed. Regrettably, both Northern and Crested Bobwhites have been more successful in the Caribbean, where Helmeted Guineafowl are also feral.

The West Indies, like other islands (*chapters 5 and 8*), have many more introductions. Puerto Rico's unfortunate record includes Canary-winged and Monk Parakeets, several amazon parrots, Orange-cheeked Waxbills, Bronze Mannikins, Scaly-breasted Munias, Java Sparrows, Village Weavers and, not least, Shiny Cowbirds and Troupials. Village Weavers are also widespread in Hispaniola, while Shiny Cowbirds are now established there and in the Lesser Antilles: their nest-parasitism is an added threat to rare endemics. Troupials – South American orioles – turn up on other islands. Similarly, Grassland Yellow Finches of Central and South America, introduced to Barbados in about 1900, subsequently spread through the Lesser Antilles.

Jamaica has Common Starlings (otherwise hardly present in the Neotropics), also Green-rumped Parrotlets (on Barbados too) and Saffron Finches from South America. In Cuba's case, it is not clear whether Red-legged Honeycreepers and Lesser Goldfinches are indigenous, or old introductions from Mexico; Black-bellied Whistling-ducks were certainly brought there.

Some West Indian birds have also been moved between islands: Carib Grackles and two of the endemic bullfinches; even Turkey Vultures were introduced to Puerto Rico from Cuba in about 1880.

More unexpected was the successful establishment of Greater Birds-of-paradise – from the Aru Islands off New Guinea – on Little Tobago in 1909, but the population eventually declined: by the late 1970s there was just one male displaying and he survived only a few more years.

Extinctions

Many of the extinct Neotropical birds were West Indian, and most of those were parrots. Of at least 28 island parrots in the Caribbean when Columbus arrived in the late fifteenth century, only a dozen survive today. Guadeloupe alone lost three endemics, and Martinique at least two. Apart from parakeets and amazons, eight or nine macaws were wiped out, mostly by the 1700s, though one of two Jamaican species lasted until the early 1800s and the Cuban Red Macaw until about 1885.

Other West Indian extinctions since 1600 have been remarkably few, considering the vulnerability of island birds (*chapters 5 and 8*): only the Grand Cayman Thrush (last recorded 1938) is certain. The Jamaican Pauraque, a nightjar related to the Least Pauraque of Hispaniola, has not been seen since 1859, but there are those who hope that such a nocturnal bird of semi-arid hill country might still exist. Semper's Warbler of St Lucia may also be extinct (*p.46*).

The only other known Neotropical extinctions are the Slender-billed Grackle (1910), an icterid with a tiny marshland range in one area of central Mexico; and two grebes, both recent. The Colombian Grebe (1977), often treated as an isolated race of the northern Black-necked but surely distinct, was confined to the region of Lago Tota, Colombia. The Atitlán Grebe (1980), like an outsize Pied-billed, was endemic to the lake of that name in the mountains of Guatemala. In addition, the Glaucous Macaw of Paraguay has not been recorded since 1955.

Threatened birds

The operative word in the previous paragraph is 'known': except on small islands or in limited open habitats like the Slender-billed Grackle's marshland – themselves 'islands' in a way – it is often difficult to be certain that a species is extinct. This applies particularly to small forest birds: some have been discovered decades after they were thought lost.

Thus, several other Neotropical birds unrecorded for a long time may or may not be extinct. The tiny Kinglet Calyptura – a cotinga somewhat reminiscent of a Ruby-crowned Kinglet or a Firecrest – was recorded from only two now largely deforested places in south-east Brazil and not this century. Also from eastern Brazil, in the Salvador area, Stresemann's Bristlefront – a tapaculo – is known only from two specimens collected a century apart in the 1830s and 1930s: probably something like a big slate-black and brown wren, it is another forest bird that may still hang on in what little suitable habitat remains. Again, the Tumaco Seedeater, a small grey and rufous bunting with black wings and tail, has not been recorded for 80 years; it lived on an inshore island now largely swallowed up by Colombia's Tumaco City.

These three are (or were) all secretive, small or inconspicuous. If not extinct, they are certainly endangered. One or two hummingbirds and a tanager are, as shown later, in a similar position.

Of over 3000 endemic Neotropical birds, some 360 – say, 12 per cent – are causing concern. This is a much higher total – though not proportion – than in any other region of the world. Two-thirds of the 30-odd essenti-

ally South and Central American and Caribbean families include threatened species.

The flightless rheas have steadily declined through persecution and the spread of ranching, though free-running Greater Rheas are bred commercially. Darwin's Rheas are not uncommon in wilder parts of the Patagonian lowlands, but the Puna Rhea which lives on high Andean slopes in south Peru and Bolivia and on the Argentine–Chilean border is now classed as 'Endangered'.

Tinamous range throughout the region, in grass or marsh, forest or mountain. Brown, grey, barred, and terrestrial, they run like guineafowl on sturdy legs and fly like partridges on rounded wings, stiff and down-curved. Formerly abundant, some tinamous are still common, but all are shy and most are mainly heard: they crouch or stand motionless until flushed, or creep away through scrub or crops. Some are seen most often on South America's new roads, standing confused as vehicles rush at them. They are also frequently shot for food. But, although the pampas species have coped with the switch to wheat, so that pesticides and harvesting have perhaps become their greatest threats, it is habitat destruction and disturbance in restricted ranges that have put seven other tinamous at risk. Half of those are forest forms and two more are restricted to Andean grassland above 2500 m.

Screamers, birds of wetland edge, have the air of design by committee: they are large, look ungainly, and are superficially goose-like but with shorter necks, longer legs, heavy rounded bodies, small heads and chicken-like bills. Once airborne, they fly well and soar to great heights. When nervous, they utter loud trumpeting calls. One of the three, the Northern Screamer, has a tiny range in north Colombia and north-west Venezuela.

The curassows and guans are among the Neotropical families most at risk: over a third of the 45-odd species are threatened to varying degrees by deforestation and uncontrolled hunting. Black-fronted Piping-guans (**11**) and Horned Guans (**12**) are both

17

HYACINTH VISORBEARER

Augastes scutatus

*Many of the 320 hummingbirds have exotic names. As military as the
visorbearers are the lancebills and sabrewings; more evocative, the
sapphires, emeralds, sunbeams, fairies and coquettes. Most are only
6–13 cm long and weigh a mere 2–9 g. Hovering at flowers, they feed on
nectar and insects with their long bills and specialised tongues, then
dart in any direction, often backwards. This particular species is
restricted to open rocky slopes in one part of east-central Brazil. The
bronzy-green and dark blue male has a shimmering golden-green black-
edged face, deep purplish side-ruff and whitish breast-band; the female
lacks the black edges and has a bluer tail and a paler breast.*

43

18

SEVEN-COLOURED TANAGER
Tangara fastuosa

'Tanager', like 'cotinga', comes from a Tupi Indian name. Related to finches and American orioles,
the tanagers and honeycreepers form a large New World group of over 240 species. Eating fruits and
insects, they tend to live in the canopy and edges, rather than the forest depths. Most are poor
songsters but brightly plumaged. This one's turqoise head, paler shoulders, and yellow-orange and
green rump contrast with a violet-blue belly, sheened tail, and black back, chest and flight-feathers,
the last edged yellow-green. It is still locally common in east Brazil, but its lowland forests are being
felled and, like other tanagers, it is excessively trapped for the cagebird trade.

'Endangered'. So are the White-winged Guan (north-west Peru), the Cauca Guan (west-central Colombia), the Red-billed Curassow (south-east Brazil), and the Alagoas Razor-billed Curassow (east Brazil), all on the verge of extinction. Indeed, the Alagoas was thought already lost until a small population was located in remnant forest; breeding from some captive birds which are held privately in Rio de Janeiro is the only way of saving this species.

The potoos are a distinct family of curious arboreal nightjars. Roosting upright on branches by day, like frogmouths, and nesting on tree-stumps, they hawk flying insects by night from perches. Three of the five species are little known, though in recent years their voices have been learned and they are proving less rare than once thought.

Each of the next three endemic families, together totalling over 100 species, includes only one that may be at risk. These are the Keel-billed Motmot (13); the Three-toed Jacamar of south-east Brazil; and the Yellow-browed Toucanet of north-central Peru. The jacamars, 15–30 cm long, are hyperactive forest and savannah birds, mostly with long bills, metallic green backs and rufous bellies, which catch insects like flycatchers or bee-eaters and nest in burrows. The Yellow-browed Toucanet is one of the smaller toucans, mainly green with a large grey-blue bill.

Turning to the endemic small birds – the passerines – the huge family of ovenbirds and spinetails (p.37) includes over 20 that are causing concern because of restricted ranges, small populations, and forest and other habitat destruction. Some of those of agricultural areas, such as the Common Miner, although not yet at risk as species, have decreased greatly in the last two decades, perhaps from pesticides.

Among the generally larger woodcreepers, Snethlage's has a highly restricted forest range in tree-shorn east Brazil; rufous and buff, it is nearly 30 cm in length, with a longish, slightly curved bill.

Being essentially forest shade-haunters, over 30 of that other huge endemic family, the antbirds (p.37), are also threatened; some have tiny or restricted distributions, in which their habitat is rapidly going. The Black-hooded Antwren (14) and the glossy-black Fringe-backed Fire-eye are classed as 'Endangered' and two other east Brazilian species as 'Vulnerable'; at least two dozen more are likely to be heading in the same direction. Several of these are antpittas – so called for their terrestrial habits, long legs and almost non-existent tails, something like the more colourful Old World pittas – and two in Colombia have not been recorded for 80 years.

Also birds of forest undergrowth, the eight gnateaters (not to be confused with the unrelated gnatcatchers) are warbler-sized, short-tailed, long-legged, and seemingly neckless. The Hooded Gnateater is yet another species with a restricted and decreasing forest range in north-east Brazil.

The tapaculos, rather variable in size and shape, are also mostly forest birds, living mainly on the ground. Two little-known species of what is left of the forests of eastern Brazil are the long-tailed Stresemann's Bristle-front (p.42) and the smaller short-tailed Brasilia Tapaculo, slate-blue and shades of grey and rufous. Like all tapaculos, these two are hard to see: they seldom fly, but run on large feet with their rather soft tails cocked. Indeed, the Brasilia Tapaculo was, like the bristlefront, originally known from only two or three specimens; then a small population was found in remnant forest near Brasilia.

Some cotingas live in scrub, savannah or plantations but most, once again, are forest species. More than a dozen of this diverse family are causing concern, and several are at best 'Vulnerable'. These include the smallest, the Kinglet Calyptura (p.42), and one of the largest, the Long-wattled Umbrellabird (15), as well as the Banded and White-winged Cotingas of south-east Brazil. These last are the size of smallish thrushes, the male Banded brilliant blue and purple, the male White-winged purplish with white wings.

Two other endemic Neotropical families with species at risk are the tit-sized manakins and the lark-sized but finch-like plantcutters. The Black-capped Manakin is maroon to rufous and black above and buff to yellow below, and the Golden-crowned green and yellow with a golden top to its head; both are Brazilian forest birds of very limited range, the first on the borders with Argentina and the second in Amazonia. The Peruvian Plantcutter is endemic to north coastal Peru, where its dry scrub habitat is being lost to cultivation.

Among families or groups characteristic of the Americas as a whole, one of the two turkeys, over 40 of the hummingbirds (*see* **16–17**), nearly 20 each of the tanagers (*see* **18**) and tyrant-flycatchers, and nearly ten each of the wood-warblers (*see also* **5–6**) and icterids, as well as one mockingbird, one thrasher, one gnat-catcher and one vireo are at least causing concern.

Relatively few of this essentially New World assortment are as yet classed as 'Endangered' or even 'Vulnerable'. The Ocellated Turkey, for example, simply seems likely to be at risk because of its restricted and patchy range in Yucatán, Chiapas, Guatemala and Belize, where, like the curassows and guans, it is overhunted and losing habitat.

Nevertheless, the Hook-billed Hermit, a small bronzy-green and cinnamon hummingbird of south-east Brazil, comes into the 'Endangered' category because so much of its restricted forest habitat has been destroyed. Two other hummingbirds, the Black-billed Hermit of Brazil and the Chilean Woodstar, are classed as 'Rare', while one or two Ecuadorean hummingbirds have not been recorded for many years and may, perhaps, even be extinct.

The Cherry-throated Tanager – if it still exists, as its known forests in south-east Brazil have been cleared – is certainly 'Endangered'. Two other forest tanagers with limited ranges – the Azure-rumped of the mountains of south Mexico and adjacent Guatemala, and the startlingly beautiful Seven-coloured (**18**) – are at least 'Vulnerable' or 'Rare'. In the latter's case, this is as much through the activities of the cagebird trade – especially bad in South America – as through deforest-

ation: this particular tanager adapts readily enough to secondary growth, but it has a tiny range.

Most of the tyrant-flycatchers causing concern are South American, except for the Belted Flycatcher of the mountains of southern Mexico and adjacent Guatemala and the rather similar Salvin's Flycatcher of eastern Nicaragua and Costa Rica. The wood-warblers in this category are a mixture of South, Central and Caribbean species. One now classed as 'Endangered' is the grey and whitish Semper's Warbler of mountain-forest undergrowth on St Lucia; indeed, it may already be extinct, perhaps because of introduced mongooses. The far more striking Whistling Warbler of St Vincent is also rare.

Several other threatened species of these all-American families are also Caribbean. Another 'Endangered' is the White-breasted Thrasher of Martinique and, again, St Lucia – sooty-brown above and pure white below – which has been reduced to a few dozen pairs by hunting and by introduced mongooses and rats. The once common but now 'Vulnerable' Yellow-shouldered Blackbird of Puerto Rico and nearby Mona has been reduced to a few hundreds by drainage (habitat loss), introduced rats (predation) and Shiny Cowbirds (nest-parasitism). Two more island icterids causing concern are the Martinique Oriole and the Monserrat Oriole, both in decline.

The gnatcatchers are a New World group of 13 minute long-tailed birds related to wrens. The blue-grey and whitish Cuban Gnatcatcher is one of several endemics of restricted range on the large island of Cuba. At the other end of the scale, Colombia's tiny Isla de San Andrés, off Nicaragua, has the scarce San Andrés Vireo living in its threatened mangroves. Elsewhere, the Socorro Mockingbird, endemic to that one island in the Revillagigedo archipelago, was thought extinct until its rediscovery in 1988.

Many of Central and South America's most threatened birds are Neotropical representatives of various cosmopolitan groups – seabirds, raptors, rails and, in particular, parrots – as well as certain of the grebes, flamingos, trogons, barbets, woodpeckers, jays and so on.

The medium-sized, grey and white Puna Grebe, endemic to Lago de Junín in the Peruvian Andes, is classed as 'Endangered'. Grebes are vulnerable to pollution and the risk is compounded by this one's evident flightlessness – like the much larger and now extinct Atitlán Grebe (*p.42*), it has never been seen to fly – and by its being confined to a single, albeit extensive, lake. The workings of a copper-mine were nearly disastrous: once abundant, the species had dropped to a few hundreds by the late 1970s. There are attempts to prevent further pollution and, when the political situation allows, it is hoped to try again to move some to smaller, safer waters.

Another grebe, not yet in danger but certainly flightless and apparently limited to the admittedly far larger Lagos de Poopó and Titicaca (along with the small Lago Umayo) in the Andes of Bolivia and Peru, is the slightly smaller Short-winged Grebe. The similar-sized Hooded Grebe was found only in 1974 and is classed as 'Rare'. Restricted to lakes in Santa Cruz, Argentina, it is more numerous than originally thought, but both need careful monitoring.

Two of the world's five flamingos are confined to the Andes. Though more mobile than these grebes and occurring in upland Peru, Bolivia, Chile and Argentina, the large Andean Flamingo and the smaller James's Flamingo breed at only a few saline mountain lakes above 2500 m or more. Each numbers tens of thousands (the Andean about 150,000), but they are at long-term risk from disturbance and pollution. Both have yellow, not pink, on the bill, while the Andean is unusual in having yellow legs.

Many penguins (*see 86*) are typical of cool far-southern waters, but the Galápagos Penguin is equatorial and two other rather similar species, both with banded head and breast patterns and some pink around their bills and eyes, are found nesting quite far north on mainland South America. The Magellanic Penguin nests on the more southerly coasts of both

Argentina and Chile, as well as on Juan Fernández; it is not threatened, but much reduced by disturbance and persecution. The Humboldt Penguin breeds mainly within the coastal tropics of Peru and Chile; with its isolated range, it is more at risk from persecution and, like most penguins, from Man's overfishing.

19

GREY-BACKED HAWK
Leucopternis occidentalis

This is one of the largest and rarest of a distinctive and threatened group of small to buzzard-sized hawks of tropical America: five of the ten species now number, at most, only a few hundreds each. Two are mainly grey, one can be almost all white; the Grey-backed and the rest are slaty above, with variously streaked heads, and white below; their tails are either dark with a white band or vice versa. They are forest raptors that swoop from a perch on to tree-snakes and lizards; some also take insects and injured birds. The Grey-backed, confined to west Equador and extreme north-west Peru, is found in tropical and subtropical forest to 1800 m; much lowland habitat has been cleared for agriculture.

Other seabirds under threat from these and other factors include the Black-capped Petrel of Hispaniola and Cuba; the Dark-rumped Petrel of Galápagos and also Hawaii (*chapter 8*); Defilippe's Petrel and the Pink-footed Shearwater of offshore Chilean islands; Townsend's Shearwater of the Revillagigedos (*see also p.31*); Markham's and Hornby's Storm-petrels of (probably) the coastal deserts of Peru and northern Chile; the Peruvian Diving-petrel of the same area; the Flightless Cormorant and Lava Gull of the Galápagos; and Olrog's Gull of coastal Argentina.

The few hundred Galápagos Flightless Cormorants do not move outside their breeding ranges on just two islands, and they are now at some risk from fishing on an industrial scale with nets. They are classed as 'Rare' and some of the others above as 'Vulnerable' or 'Endangered' because of restricted ranges, Man's interference and, with island species, predation and damage by introduced rats and other mammals.

Like other tropical lands, Central and South America are rich in birds of prey. The Neotropics as a whole

have around 100 species of diurnal raptors, nearly a third of the world's total, and at least 20 are threatened. In contrast, the region holds only a quarter of the world's owls (though forest species are still being discovered) and, as yet, none is at particular risk.

Three of the rare raptors are island buzzards: the Galápagos, Juan Fernández and Ridgway's Hawks. The first two are large buzzards endemic to the islands off Ecuador and Chile whose names they bear; the third is a small species confined to Hispaniola in the Caribbean. On adjacent Cuba, Wilson's Kite (a yellow-billed race of the mainland Hook-billed) and Gundlach's Hawk (a largish endemic accipiter related to the North American Cooper's Hawk) must also be classed as 'Rare'. Each of these five birds has a population of two or three hundred at most.

Several mainland hawks are also at considerable risk because of limited ranges, often associated with fast-disappearing forest habitat. Four of the 'white hawks' come into this category: the Grey-backed (**19**); the Plumbeous of Panama to north-west Peru, rather small

and mainly dark slate; and the White-necked and Mantled Hawks of, chiefly, eastern Brazil, which are bigger and dark-backed but otherwise extensively white. All four are largely confined to humid forest in areas where there has been much clearance.

The same applies to the Semicollared Hawk, a rare accipiter of subtropical mountain forest in Colombia and Ecuador; this is the upland replacement of the widespread Tiny Hawk – sometimes as little as 20 cm in length – which even preys on hummingbirds.

On the other hand, the Grey-bellied Hawk (an accipiter), the Crowned and Black Solitary-eagles (large buzzards, not true eagles) and the really large Crested and Harpy Eagles all have wide distributions in mainly tropical South America and yet are everywhere scarce to rare. The last three, indeed, extend up into Central America but there they are becoming ever rarer because of their need for large areas of primary rainforest. The Crowned Solitary-eagle is actually an open-woodland and savannah bird, but too sluggish and tame for its own good.

One other rare and little-known upland buzzard of the cold–temperate south is the Rufous-tailed Hawk, a

20
LONG-TRAINED NIGHTJAR
Macropsalis creagra

The nightjars are a worldwide family of some 80 species. All have big eyes, tiny bills but huge gapes, and small feet hardly designed for walking: the first two are adaptations for a nocturnal life and taking insects in flight; and strong feet are unnecessary for birds that, camouflaged in buff, rufous, grey and black, spend the day on the ground or along a branch. Many are declining through deforestation, drainage, and pesticides. Confined to south-east Brazil, this is one of five in South America at risk from habitat damage. Its elongated outer tail-feathers add 50 cm to a real length of only 20 cm; the males of several species use such feathers on wings or tail in display flights.

close relative of the widespread Red-tailed Hawk of North America.

Two of a secretive forest group of atypical falcons – the Plumbeous Forest-falcon (borders of Colombia and Ecuador) and Buckley's Forest-falcon (borders of Amazonian Ecuador and Peru) – have very restricted distributions and are apparently uncommon. The range of the strikingly plumaged Orange-breasted Falcon extends very sporadically in forest areas with cliffs through Central and South America down as far as northern Argentina, but it is generally rare and in some countries probably extinct; many supposed sightings turn out to be of the rather similar but significantly smaller Bat Falcon.

None of the South American vultures is under real threat, though large areas of, for example, agricultural Argentina now lack the formerly more widespread Black and Turkey Vultures. This might be thought due to pesticides or other poisoning, but in that case it is remarkable how common is another carrion-eater, the omnivorous Chimango Caracara. Although restricted to the southern third of South America, north to Paraguay and so largely outside the tropics, this is one of the 15 most numerous raptors in the world; in the agricultural regions, indeed, it is everywhere and often 50 or more can be seen feeding with and like gulls behind a ploughing tractor.

The partridges are replaced in the New World by the distinct American quails. Two have tiny ranges in the Colombian Andes: the Gorgeted Wood-quail of the temperate zone, known chiefly from one forest of some 1200 square km, is classed as 'Endangered', but the position of the Chestnut Wood-quail of the subtropical zone is indeterminate.

The cosmopolitan family of rails and gallinules is much more typically Neotropical; indeed, eight of the world's ten coots live there. But only three of this family are classed even as 'Vulnerable' or 'Rare' in the region: the undistinguished-looking Bogotá Rail of the temperate zone of the Colombian Andes; the rare Zapata Rail of one swamp in Cuba; and the Horned

21

RESPLENDENT QUETZAL

Pharomachrus mocinno

*Two-thirds of the 40 or so trogons live in tropical
America. Many males (see 9) are glittering green with
crimson bellies, often patterned white and black
undertails, and maybe yellow or red bills; females are
much duller. The five known as quetzals ('ket-saals')
have helmet-like crests and variously elongated wing-
and tail-coverts that on the male Resplendent form
flexible streamers up to two-thirds of a metre long.
Living in damp mountain forests from Mexico to
Panama, it snatches fruits, insects, frogs and snails in
fluttering sallies. Sacred to the Mayas and Aztecs, it is
now Guatemala's 'National Bird', but vulnerable to
deforestation and trapping for the cagebird trade.*

Coot, confined to the Andes above 3000 m where
Bolivia, Chile and Argentina meet. Additionally, the
Austral Rail of Patagonia should be classed as 'Endangered' since it has not been recorded for several
decades. Another four South American rails and crakes
evidently have limited ranges and restricted habitats,
but these secretive birds are often difficult to assess.

Doves and pigeons are abundant in the Neotropics,
and a total of 63 species represents over one-fifth of the
world figure. Some that have adapted well to Man's
environments are exceedingly common, but eight are
rare or have very restricted ranges. Of these, the
Grenada Dove, the Blue-headed and Grey-headed
Quail-doves of Cuba and the Dominican Republic, and
the Ring-tailed Pigeon of Jamaica are Caribbean
endemics facing all the problems of island species in
general and of pigeons in particular (*chapters 5 and 8*).

The rather small Tolima Dove of the Colombian
Andes and its relative, the Ochre-bellied Dove of the
lowland border of Ecuador and Peru, are, once again,
forest birds of limited distributions and disappearing
habitats. The tiny Blue-eyed Ground-dove, only 15 cm
long and confined to the Brazilian tableland, in a region
of stunted gnarled trees with tangled undergrowth and
more open grass, is rare and has apparently withdrawn
from neighbouring habitats. The slightly larger Purple-
winged Ground-dove, of south-east Brazil and, marginally, adjacent Paraguay and Argentina, is another
terrestrial dove of wooded thickets that is decreasing
and now classed as 'Vulnerable'.

Of five threatened woodpeckers, two are 'Endangered'. One, the little-known Helmeted Woodpecker is
restricted to forest remnants in south-east Brazil and
adjacent Paraguay and Argentina. The other is the
large and spectacular Ivory-billed Woodpecker, formerly found also in the United States (*p.28*) but now
reduced to a handful of pairs in Cuba.

A number of other more cosmopolitan families have
a few threatened representatives in Central and South
America. These include two ducks, the Brazilian
Merganser of forested rivers in one small area of Brazil,

Paraguay and Argentina, and the West Indian Whistling-duck; two cuckoos, one the rare Cocos Cuckoo endemic to the Isla del Coco, half-way between Costa Rica and the Galápagos; five nightjars, one the Long-trained (**20**); the White-chested Swift of Colombia's Cauca Valley; two trogons, one the Resplendent Quetzal (**21**, *see also* 9); and two barbets, one the Toucan Barbet (**22**).

Among threatened passerines are two island swallows of the Caribbean; two rare pipits of the borders of Argentina, Paraguay and Brazil; the Rufous-throated Dipper, endemic to north Andean Argentina; four wrens, two of which are confined to the Colombian Andes, one to south-east Mexico, and the last to a single swamp in Cuba; the Rufous-brown Solitaire, a forest thrush known from a few widely scattered areas of South America; an assortment of some 25 buntings and finches, including the Tumaco Seedeater (*p.42*); and four rather colourful jays. Some of these birds are not yet known to be actually endangered, but restricted ranges, forest habitats and other factors make it likely that they are at risk.

Some of the finches are of particular interest. Two of the Galápagos tree-finches – one endemic to Santa María, and the other to the mangroves of Isabela and Fernandina – have declining or very restricted populations: of the 14 Darwin's finches, these are the two most at risk. The only Neotropical finch actually classed as 'Endangered' is the Red Siskin, which has a small range in north Venezuela and the north-east Colombian border area. Its downfall has been its striking orange-red plumage with contrasting black head, wings and tail: this has made it a prime target for a cagebird trade which seems to be bent on exterminating it in the wild.

But, of all the Neotropical bird families, whether endemic or representative of more cosmopolitan groups, the parrots are as a whole the most threatened. They exemplify the problems that beset this region: a majority live in lowland tropical forest; and many are popular cagebirds, some fetching thousands of dollars.

22
TOUCAN BARBET
Semnornis ramphastinus

Barbets – big-headed, stout-billed, short-tailed – feed on fruits and insects, and excavate holes in trees, banks or termite mounds. Most of some 80 species live in forest or savannah in Africa and south Asia; a dozen in tropical America. Many are adaptable to Man's world and not yet at risk. But the Toucan Barbet of west Colombia and Ecuador is threatened by deforestation and cagebird trapping. Named for its thick cream and dusky bill, it is under 20 cm long, stocky and neckless, with grey and black head, white behind the eyes, yellow rump, and red to yellow breast. It cocks its tail while about-facing. Barbets are noisy: this one's rhythmic honks, often in duet, carry a kilometre.

PARROTS, THE CAGEBIRD TRADE, AND LEAR'S MACAW

Anodorhynchus leari

Macaws are medium-sized to very large South American forest and savannah parrots. Some of the 16 species are a mass of primary colours. Lear's Macaw – after Edward Lear, humorist, artist and ornithologist – is a relatively restrained purplish-blue with rich cobalt wings and tail, and yellow spectacles. Until a tiny population of 60 was found in 1978, it was known only from occasional captives in consignments of Hyacinth Macaws – among the biggest of all parrots, up to 100 cm in length, and a regular target for the trappers.

About 140 parrots – out of some 350 – are Neotropical, one or two breeding down into Patagonia and even Tierra del Fuego. They come in many shapes and sizes. Some are chunky and stubby-tailed, while the parakeets are slim and, like the macaws, have long pointed tails. The tiny parrotlets are one-eighth as big as the largest macaws. Greens are the commonest colours, often gaudily mixed with blues, yellows, oranges and reds.

Parrots have strong curved bills for crushing food, used also as a third 'foot' for gripping twigs; their true feet have two toes forward and two back. Some are found on shores, or by open streams, or on barren mountains, but the majority are forest birds living on seeds, fruits, nectar, and insects. Most are gregarious and noisy, and fly with fast shallow beats. They nest in holes: usually hollow trees, but, for example, Burrowing Parrots dig their own in earth faces and colonies of Monk Parakeets build vast conglomerations of sticks.

With their bright colours and cheery screeches, parrots have long been popular cagebirds. For this and other reasons – notably deforestation – 70 species are now at risk, half of them in the tropical Americas. The past 15 years have seen growing publicity about the iniquities of the cagebird trade. Many birds perish in international transit. Sometimes thousands are left for days in cramped conditions at airports. They suffer stress, heat or cold, dehydration, inadequate water, and no food; weakened and crowded, they are open to disease. Many that last the journey die in quarantine before ever reaching the shops. Others never acclimatise, not surviving their first year.

In 1984–88, 72,000 Orange-winged Amazons were exported from South America and 230,000 Grey Parrots from West Africa: of those reaching the UK, 19 per cent and 9 per cent were dead. In 1988 alone, 7 per cent of almost 1000 Alder Parrots imported into Britain died – they have a restricted range in south-east Bolivia and north Argentina – and 368 of 464 White-fronted Amazons from Honduras were dead on arrival or died in quarantine. Mixed cargoes of thousands of other birds have had 10–15 per cent dead. Sometimes over 50 per cent of finches, white-eyes and such specialist feeders as sunbirds expire in transit or quarantine. Whole consignments of hummingbirds have been dead on arrival.

These figures apply only to the international transit and quarantine stages. They can take no account of capture and subsequent cross-country journeys. It has been estimated that, for every cagebird of wild origin in the shops, up to four others have died on the way. Europe alone imports more than 3 million birds annually; North America and Japan are as bad. South America, Africa and south-east Asia are major sources, Bangkok the most notorious of the clearing houses.

Of nearly 140 South and Central American and Caribbean parrots, parakeets and macaws – 40 per cent of the world's total – as many as a quarter are causing concern to some degree; nine are already classed as 'Endangered'.

Among the last are two of the 16 macaws, Spix's and Lear's (**23**). Long confined to ancient caraiba gallery woodland on the borders of two states in north-east Brazil, Spix's Macaw has been harried by bird-trappers to the point where only a single bird survives in the wild. Another, Wagler's Macaw of southern Bolivia and possibly north-west Argentina, is known only from museum skins and cagebirds, and has yet to be seen in the wild by ornithologists. Three more macaws – the Hyacinth, Red-fronted and Blue-winged – are drastically declining in numbers from a combination of trapping and deforestation.

At the other end of the size scale, three of the seven parrotlets seem at risk. Sparrow-sized but much more compact, the Black-eared of south-east Brazil is already classed as 'Rare' through the disappearance of its forests. Also causing concern are the Golden-tailed Parrotlet, restricted to forest in eastern Brazil, and the Spot-winged, a mountain species of the middle subtropical Andean slopes of Colombia and Ecuador. Like most parrots, these parrotlets live on seeds, berries, fruits and nuts.

In between these size extremes comes a whole series of other parrots that are variously threatened. Some, such as the Rufous-fronted Parakeet of mountain scrub in the Andes of Colombia, are not colourful and probably not endangered by the trappers, but have lost much habitat. Others, such as the Rusty-faced Parrot of the Andes from Ecuador northwards, are simply rather rare and very little known. For many of the species, however, such as the Grey-cheeked Parrot of the borders of Ecuador and Peru, serious decreases are due to a combination of habitat damage and trapping.

One group of over 40 medium-sized parakeets with long pointed tails are often called 'conures'. Two of these, the Golden Conure (**24**) of Brazilian forest and

the Yellow-eared of subtropical Andean palms in Colombia and Ecuador, are already 'Vulnerable' and seven more are causing concern. Most conures are green with perhaps a little yellow or patches of another colour, but the Golden is one of two that are strikingly golden-yellow; it has green flight-feathers, while the yellow northern race of the Sun Conure in Venezuela, the Guianas and Brazil has the cheeks and belly orange-red and the flight-feathers and tail blue and green. The latter is a bird of palms, savannah, scrub and grassland, while the Golden is a forest bird of limited range. Both are victims of the trappers for the cagebird trade, and the Golden suffers from the additional problem of habitat destruction.

A comparable group of nearly 30 short-tailed parrots are known as 'amazons'. Only about a quarter actually live in the Amazon basin – indeed, half are confined to Central America or the West Indies – but the term is applied to all the parrots of the genus *Amazona*, most of which are mainly green with bright patches of other colours. A dozen seem at risk and no fewer than six are already 'Endangered'. The latter include five of the nine endemic to mainly mountain forests of the West Indies: the Puerto Rican, St Lucia and St Vincent Amazons, and the Red-necked and Imperial of Dominica.

All these colourful amazons have been greatly reduced by the combined effects of trapping and nest-robbing for the cagebird trade, of shooting, and of forest destruction or at least the removal of the old trees that provide nest-holes. Forest clearance on Caribbean islands also puts at greater risk the remaining trees from hurricanes, and the remaining birds either from predation by introduced rats or from competition for breeding places with the Pearly-eyed Thrashers that prey on the amazons' nests. Three of the West Indian amazons now have populations in the low hundreds, and the Imperial and Puerto Rican are dangerously down to a few tens. Captive-breeding projects, already started in two or three cases, may be helpful safeguards.

The last of the amazons already 'Endangered' is the Red-tailed, of remnant forest in south-east Brazil. It exemplifies the threats affecting so many of South America's birds: it has a limited range; it is a forest species from an area where there has been drastic tree clearance; and, although protected by law, it is still trapped for the cagebird trade.

It also stands as an example of the dozen threatened endemic parrots of north-east, east and south-east Brazil where habitat destruction has been particularly bad. The others are Spix's and Lear's Macaws; Golden, Golden-capped and Pearly Conures; Blue-chested Parakeet; Red-browed and Yellow-faced Amazons; Purple-bellied Parrot; and two of the three parrotlets mentioned. An unlucky thirteenth might be one of two other amazons of south-east Brazil – the Red-spectacled or the Vinaceous – which just hang on also in extreme north-east Argentina and either south-east Paraguay or north Uruguay. Can enough be saved in eastern South America between the mouths of the Amazon and the Rio de la Plata before it is too late?

24
GOLDEN CONURE
Aratinga guarouba

About 40 of South America's parakeets are known as 'conures'. This one – here against a spray of blue epiphytic orchids – has a very limited forest range in north-east Brazil south of the Amazon's deltas. All golden-yellow but for green flight-feathers, it has long been a target for the cagebird trade and had become relatively rare even 50 years ago. Now, in the face of growing forest destruction, its range is more fragmented. Some open-country parakeets are successful in Man's damaged environment. The forest species, less able to adapt, are not: the Golden Conure, already classed as 'Vulnerable', is in danger of extinction unless some habitat is preserved and the trapping stopped.

Europe, North Africa, and Asia north of the Himalayas

The Palearctic ('old northern') here covers all of Europe, including Iceland, and the whole of arctic and temperate Asia, including Japan, together with Greenland and North Africa.

Greenland comes in because, although geographically part of North America, it shares more birds, invertebrates and plants (but not mammals) with the northern Palearctic. There are, however, many affinities between the animals and plants of arctic and temperate North America and Eurasia in general, and it is often convenient to refer to the Nearctic and Palearctic together as the Holarctic ('whole northern').

In the eastern Atlantic, the Palearctic takes in the Azores, Madeira, the Canaries and, even though they actually lie within the tropics, the Cape Verdes, whose avifauna is more typical of this northern region. At the other end of the landmass, the west Bering and west Pacific islands south to the Japanese archipelagos of Ogasawara-shotō (Bonin Islands), Iwo Jima and Kazan-rettō (Volcano Islands) also form part, but the Nansei-shotō (Ryūkyū Islands) and, more especially, Taiwan are excluded (*chapter 6*).

In northern Africa and south Asia, the southern boundary of the Palearctic is ill-defined because the characteristic families of animals and plants merge, rather than switch abruptly, into those of the Afrotropical and Indomalayan regions (*chapters 4 and 6*). In general terms, the boundary passes across the central Sahara, up the Red Sea, across northern Saudi Arabia, along coastal Iran, up through central Pakistan, along the Himalayan ridge, through northernmost Burma and north-west Yunnan, and thence the length of the Chang Jiang (Yangtze) to the China coast.

With a total area of nearly 35 million square km, the Palearctic is about half as big again as the Nearctic, and easily the largest of the regions. Like the Nearctic, it spans over 60 degrees of latitude from well north of the Arctic Circle to a little south of the Tropic of Cancer; more remarkably, it stretches across 260 degrees of longitude. Thus, it has a wide range of climates and there are great differences, because of the airflow patterns, between the western and eastern extremes.

Mean temperatures in January and July differ by no more than $10°C$ over much of Europe and only by $12°C$ in Iceland, but in North Africa the difference is $20°C$ and in north-east Norway up to $40°C$ or more. Winters are much colder north, east and south of the Baltic. The bulk of Palearctic Asia has a greater range of means, from $0°$ to $-20°C$ in January up to $20-30°C$ in July. It remains above freezing in some more southerly areas in winter and there the summer means may be up to $40°C$, hottest in the west Asian deserts.

The broad arctic strip along the top, where July temperatures are mostly below $10°C$, includes the coldest permanently inhabited parts of the world: at Verkhoyansk in north-east Siberia, the January mean is as low as $-50°C$ (July's $15°C$ thus differs by a remarkable $65°C$). As in the northern Nearctic, these low winter temperatures of northern Eurasia mean that the vast majority of birds have to be migratory.

In broad physical terms, the Palearctic is a multi-layered cake. The far north, right across, is a wide band of treeless tundra which, with that of Alaska and Canada, forms a circumpolar belt that is the summer breeding ground of vast numbers of wildfowl and waders. Below that is a band of mainly coniferous

forest, or taiga, that gives way in Europe to mixed and broadleaved woodland, now patchworked by agriculture and building, and in central Asia to open grassland, or steppe, increasingly desiccated and ploughed. The last two layers, which cross in Asia, are the mountain ranges that stretch from the Atlas and the Pyrenees to the Himalayas, and the belt of deserts from the Sahara to the Gobi. Each layer extends for 10–15,000 km.

Mountains commonly reach well over 3000 m in the west, from the Atlas to the Caucasus, with many peaks between 4000 and 4500 m or more. In the east, the Himalayas and the high uplands of central Asia include ridges and peaks to nearly twice those heights. The Himalayan area has eight peaks over 8000 m and, with China and the southern states of the former USSR, another dozen over 7000 m.

The Chang Jiang that forms the region's south-east boundary is the world's third longest river. Farther

25
DALMATIAN PELICAN
Pelecanus crispus

Caricatured as clumsy, but majestic in gliding like flying-boats, pelicans have heavy bodies, long necks, big bills and coloured pouches. Of the seven species worldwide, all fish-eaters, only the American Brown is marine. The rest – all white or greyish with blacker wings – inhabit fresh or brackish waters, often far inland. The Dalmatian has long gone from Dalmatia: the once huge colonies from the Balkans to Mongolia now total under 1000 pairs; and the Danube's 'millions' are down to 100 pairs. Often nesting at smaller and more accessible lakes, it suffers from drainage, pollution, water-sports, and human persecution. Colonies may have to be in reserves to survive.

26
SWINHOE'S EGRET
Egretta eulophotes

*Several of the dozen or so mostly smallish herons
known as egrets are white with plumes on head,
breast and back when nesting. Last century, these
plumes – as 'aigrettes' for women's hats – nearly
proved their downfall. Protection and education have
revived most species – but not Swinhoe's. Its main
Chinese colonies have gone, though a few still nest
near Shanghai and in Hong Kong; the last group of
any size is North Korean; the total may be under 300
pairs. In summer it has black legs and yellow feet like
Little and Snowy Egrets, but a yellow bill; in winter,
when it occurs south to Sulawesi (Celebes), the legs
are greenish, like those of white Reef Egrets, and the
bill dusky with a yellowish base.*

north in China the Hwang He (Yellow River) is also
among the top dozen, as is the Amur that runs along
the northern border of Manchuria. Also between 4400
and 5500 km in length are several of those great north-
flowing Asian rivers – the Ob-Irtysh, the Yenisei-
Angara, and the Lena – whose lower reaches and
estuaries flowing into the Arctic Sea are important
breeding grounds for wetland birds. The east-flowing
rivers of China are grossly overpopulated along their
lower reaches.

Apart from the saline Caspian and Aral Seas, Baykal
and Balkhash are among the world's 15 largest lakes.
Most of these inland seas and large fresh or brackish
lakes are increasingly polluted or partly drained. Many
rivers and smaller lakes are also heavily polluted.

Indigenous birds

The Palearctic has almost 1100 indigenous species
of breeding birds. This is considerably more than
the Nearctic, but actually slightly less for the relative

sizes of the two regions: about 31 species per million square km, as against 34. Migrants, vagrants and introductions increase the Palearctic total by a further 140 or so to over 1200.

Thus, the two northern regions, size for size, have very comparable avifaunas, both much smaller in proportional numbers of species than those of any of the four tropical and southerly continental regions. The comparable figures for breeding species per million square km in the Afrotropical, Australasian, Neotropical and Indomalayan regions are around 65, 155, 175 and 195 respectively. The northern regions of the world also have significantly lower proportions of passerines, or perching birds.

The Palearctic and Nearctic not only show marked similarities, but also share over 150 species, mainly larger birds. But the breeding birds of the Palearctic represent some 84 families, considerably more than in North America, thus indicating a greater diversity. Some 35 of these are more or less worldwide families. Among the others are a number that are characteristic of the Old World as a whole, but largely or entirely missing from the Americas.

Storks, larks, wagtails and pipits, shrikes, dippers, typical warblers, treecreepers and true sparrows are all far better represented by species and more widespread in the Palearctic: for example, there are 15 pipits and six wagtails against three and two in the Nearctic (most of those only in Alaska), and over two dozen indigenous larks opposed to just one. In contrast, there is but one wren in the Palearctic as against 16 in the Nearctic.

Families which are represented in the Palearctic but missing from the Nearctic include the flamingos, guineafowls, buttonquails, bustards, thick-knees, pratincoles and coursers, sandgrouse, bee-eaters, rollers, hoopoes, pittas, cuckoo-shrikes, bulbuls, bush-shrikes, accentors, parrotbills, Old World flycatchers, monarchs, fantails, babblers, wallcreepers, flowerpeckers, sunbirds, white-eyes, Old World orioles, starlings and true sparrows – though the last two have been introduced in North America – and such significant groups from larger families as the Old World vultures and the pheasants.

Nearly 160 Palearctic species are shared with the Afrotropical region, and over 400 with the Indomalayan. Many of these belong to widespread families of the Old World, but the size of the Indomalayan share is greatly exaggerated by mountain species in the Himalayan area that just extend from one region into the other: only a little over 200 of the species shared with the Indomalayan region are truly Palearctic.

Among the shared families are some more typical of sub-Saharan Africa or Asia. Apart from the Ostrich, now virtually extinct outside tropical Africa, they include buttonquails, parakeets, bee-eaters, cuckoo-shrikes and minivets, bulbuls, sunbirds, flowerpeckers, white-eyes, and drongos. Most of these are in the south-east Palearctic, a few in the south-west.

There are also a number of individual representatives of other southern groups. China and, in some cases, Mongolia, Manchuria or Japan are, for example, the northern limits of the Mountain Hawk Eagle, Watercock, Pheasant-tailed Jacana, Common Painted-snipe, Ibisbill, and Blue-winged Pitta. And the Ogasawara Honeyeater is an isolated representative of a widespread Australasian and Pacific family.

Similarly, in the south-west of the region, African Darters reach southern Turkey and Iraq; Black-shouldered Kites breed in North Africa, Iberia and France; Dark Chanting-goshawks and Helmeted Guineafowls have isolated populations in Morocco, as do Purple Swamphens in Mediterranean Europe, Crab-plovers in Iraq, and Senegal Coucals in Egypt. None of these, however, extends anywhere near as far north as do the American tropical influences, such as the hummingbirds and tyrant-flycatchers found in Canada and even Alaska.

No family of birds is endemic to the Palearctic. All the divers breed in the region, but all also in the Nearctic. Over one-third of pheasants are Palearctic (almost all the others being Indomalayan). The same

27
CRESTED IBIS
Nipponia nippon

Ibises have long downcurved bills and partly or entirely bare heads, also long necks and longish legs. The plumage may be black, chestnut, scarlet, pied or white. Some of the two dozen species are not pretty (28, 71), but the Crested Ibis's white or smoky-grey feathering and red face and legs redress the balance. Sadly, it is one of the rarest. It used to nest at wooded lakes and swamps across the 3000 km from west China to Japan; now all that remains is a tiny colony in China and some curiously unsuccessful captive-breeding programmes. Shooting and other persecution of a conspicuous bird, coupled with cutting and drainage of forested wetlands, appear the main causes of the decline.

applies to half each of the grouse (the rest Nearctic and two shared), of the cranes (*see* **29**), and of the sandgrouse (most of the others Afrotropical); and more than three-quarters of the auks (mostly shared with the Nearctic). Among the last are a number found on both sides of the Bering Strait. As one might expect, it is extreme north-east Siberia and Alaska, where the two continents are less than 100 km apart, that show the strongest links between the northern regions.

Few songbird families are essentially Palearctic, but the accentors (including the Dunnock) are almost confined to the region: one is just Afrotropical, in the Yemen, and several others are marginally Indo-malayan, breeding in the Himalayas or Taiwan and wintering farther south. The region holds about one-quarter of the typical thrushes; one-third each of the larks and of the wagtails and pipits; about a half of the nuthatches; and two-thirds or more of all the leaf-warblers, treecreepers and typical buntings. Just over 450 species are endemic to the Palearctic, but the avifauna as a whole is somewhat transitional between those of the Afrotropical and Indomalayan regions on the one hand, and the Nearctic on the other.

The Palearctic and Nearctic are both relatively poor in numbers of species and families. These two large regions have only 12 per cent and 8 per cent of the world's birds as breeding species. Less than one-fifth of all birds are found north of the Tropic of Cancer – a proportion that drops to well under one-sixth if the marginal species be excluded – in what amounts to over two-fifths of the world's habitable landmass. Individual species are, however, often particularly abundant in the far north in summer.

Introductions

Considering the number of European species naturalised elsewhere in the world (*especially chapters 1, 4, 5, 7 and 8*), it may seem surprising how few birds have been successfully introduced to the Palearctic. Or perhaps it is not surprising, since nostalgia has always been one of the main reasons for

28
NORTHERN BALD IBIS
Geronticus eremita

Glossed metallic green, and coppery on the shoulders, this untidy dark ibis with a dull red head and straggly ruff is the antithesis of the Crested (27) in colour and habitat. Both it and the redder-capped and short-ruffed Southern Bald Ibis of South Africa are unusual in nesting on cliffs, not wetlands, and in feeding on dry grassland, not marshes. But for single small colonies in Algeria and Turkey, this bird now breeds only in Morocco. In Turkey, hundreds in the 1950s crashed to less than 40 in the 1960s and a mere handful today; over 600 died in 1959–60, probably from pesticides. In Morocco, small colonies of coast and mountain are decreasing, perhaps from shooting and disturbance.

29

THREATS FACING CRANES,
AND THE SIBERIAN WHITE CRANE

Grus leucogeranus

Cranes are among the tallest and stateliest of all birds – long-necked, long-legged, and slender-bodied. In addition, all except the Crowned Cranes of Africa have the innermost flight-feathers of the wings lengthened and often curved into a loose ornamental train that, when the bird is settled, covers both the wing-tips and the tail. This train, or 'cloak-tail', is sometimes mistaken for the real tail.

The 15 species of cranes are represented in all the continents of the Old World, as well as in North America (*see* 1), but more than half breed only in central and eastern Asia, these mostly wintering in India or from China to Japan. Thus, the family is notably oriental and particularly characteristic of the eastern Palearctic.

Because of the patchy distributions of most cranes, their need of secluded wetlands for breeding, and their inability to tolerate disturbance, at least five species are now at risk. Drainage, land development, increasing human populations in the winter quarters and, in some areas, shooting (especially on migration) are the main threats. Each population of cranes has traditional breeding and wintering areas, and the young evidently learn from their parents the migration routes and stopovers; thus, extinction at a local level is an ever-present danger.

Four of the Palearctic cranes are classed as 'Vulnerable' and the Siberian White as 'Endangered'. With its all-white plumage, but for the black wing-ends largely or entirely hidden by the train of elongated feathers when the bird is settled, this is also one of the most striking to look at; the bare reddish skin of the forehead, appearing almost raw, surrounds ivory-white to pinkish-yellow eyes; bill and legs, too, are dull red.

Usually the bird appears as immaculately snow-white as any of the white egrets, but sometimes head and neck are stained rusty by the ferrous content of the waters in which it feeds. Though not as big as the Sarus of India and south-east Asia, this is also one of the largest cranes: it stands over 1.4 m high, not far short of the 5-foot mark; and its wing-span, at 2·2–2·6 m, is around 8 feet.

At one time this magnificent bird probably nested from just east of the Urals right across Asia, in suitable areas, to the Indigirka river and perhaps northern Manchuria. Now breeding has been fragmented into two relatively small regions of Siberia. The first is around the Ob and Irtysh rivers: this group, large enough in the nineteenth century to produce records of up to 300 on migration in the Volga delta alone, is now reduced to 20 or fewer in total, wintering mainly in the reserve of Bharatpur in north India.

The other group, over 3000 km to the east in Yakutskaya, near the Lena river, winters in eastern China, traditionally in the valley of the Chang Jiang (Yangtze) though much of that region now has too heavy a human population; even so, as many as 1400 Siberian White Cranes have been reported at the large lake of Poyang Hu.

This is a bird of vast shallow swamps and wet tundra. Each pair needs a large territory and breeding success is often low, sometimes through the activities of domesticated reindeer. The breeding

and wintering areas are otherwise protected, but some Siberian White Cranes are evidently still shot on migration: such a large and conspicuous bird presumably makes a tantalising target. The long-term position is unclear, but eggs from captive Siberian White Cranes have been hatched in nests of Common Cranes in Siberia and such artificial measures for maintaining the species may have to be extended (*see* **1**).

The Siberian White is the most aquatic and, although omnivorous, one of the most vegetarian of all cranes, often wading in shallows half a metre deep to search with head submerged for buds and roots of water plants. Some other cranes feed more on shoots and seeds of terrestrial plants, and still others more on such animal matter as insects, worms, fish, frogs, young birds and eggs, and small mammals.

Like most cranes, the Siberian White lays two eggs in an often quite bulky nest in marshland; these take about a month to hatch. The chicks run around as soon as they are dry, but it is well over two months more before they are fledged and ready to move south as a family. Unless each parent takes charge of one chick, often only the stronger of the two is reared. Fledged youngsters are rufous-buff on the fully feathered head and neck, and otherwise dull white tinged and mottled with cinnamon.

deliberate introductions and Europe has historically exported, rather than imported, human colonists. Moreover, the world's most successful introductions – Common Starlings and House Sparrows – are naturally widespread here.

This shortage of artificial species is a bonus in conservation terms: introductions are potential disasters and, in the light of modern knowledge, only carefully planned *re*introductions are acceptable. In fact, hardly any small birds have ever really become established through introductions in the Palearctic: the one or two species of African waxbills now feral in Portugal are obvious exceptions. With the size of the cagebird trade, it is not surprising that local and usually temporary populations of, especially, finches and weavers do establish themselves through escapes or releases from captivity. But, because there is generally no niche available, they tend to die out after a few years: there may be too many competitors, and climate, habitat and food have to be suitable.

Such birds as have been naturalised in the Palearctic, especially in Britain and Japan, have been mainly for food or shooting and, in Britain, as embellishments for country estates. Feral Pigeons have had an indigenous trans-Eurasian range greatly expanded and developed through long domestication, originally for food. Otherwise the obvious example in the 'food or shooting' category is the Common Pheasant. Almost entirely Asiatic in origin, it was gradually introduced to various European countries over 2000 years, though it later died out in much of the Mediterranean region.

Similarly, the south-west European Red-legged Partridge was introduced as a gamebird in Britain (and on some Atlantic islands), and the Barbary Partridge on Gibraltar and elsewhere, while there have been more recent attempts to establish the south Palearctic Chukar (and hybrids) in Britain, France and other countries. Elsewhere, the Chinese Bamboo-partridge was first naturalised in Japan about the 1920s and, much earlier, the Helmeted Guineafowl of Africa was established in the Cape Verdes.

Other alien pheasants in the west are mainly for ornamental reasons and Chinese in origin: Golden and Lady Amherst's in Britain; and Reeves's in Czechoslovakia. Earlier feral populations of Reeves's Pheasants in France, Germany and elsewhere have usually proved ephemeral, as have attempts at introducing Bobwhites and California Quails from North America.

Among ornamental wildfowl, the natural Eurasian range of the Mute Swan – even more than that of the Rock Pigeon – is clouded by a long history of feral or semi-feral breeding. Canada Geese from North America have been introduced and gradually naturalised over the past 300 years, first in Britain and then in Fenno-Scandia. Egyptian Geese from Africa (including Palearctic Egypt) have been naturalised in East Anglia since the eighteenth century, but the Bar-headed Geese from India that used to nest ferally in Sweden appear to have died out.

Mandarin Ducks from eastern Asia were deliberately released to become established in Britain, but the feral population of Ruddy Ducks from North America is probably entirely the result of escapes from captivity. Considering the number of, admittedly,

30
RED-CROWNED CRANE
Grus japonensis

Several hundreds of these fine birds – white with black forehead, neck and 'train', and a patch of red on the head – nest in Manchuria and Ussuriland, and winter mainly in Korea. Another population is resident in a single wetland area of Hokkaido, the northernmost large island of Japan. In Japan as a whole, they were commoner and far more widespread until the 1860s, but by 1900 were thought to have been hunted to extinction. Then a few were found in Kuccharo marsh in 1924 and, with protection, these have built up to over 350. Even so, the possibility of land development remains a threat; overhead cables also kill some. The species breeds well in captivity, thus providing a reserve stock.

31
SCALY-SIDED MERGANSER
Mergus squamatus

This is a rare sawbill-duck of Amurland in eastern Asia. The male has the shape and flight-pattern of a Red-breasted Merganser, but a longer crest, and the white breast of a Goosander; both sexes also show grey scale-like flank-markings. Nesting in holes in trees by fast rivers in upland forests, the species has declined since the mid 1960s to only a few hundred pairs. Causes may include forest management and clearance, pollution, river disturbance, and predations of feral mink. Unlike its common relatives, this duck is also unusually territorial, each pair needing at least 4 km of river, and thus thinly spread. In winter most move to lower reaches, but in hard weather some go to Korea and China.

usually pinioned ornamental waterfowl in Britain and Ireland, it is perhaps surprising that more species do not escape in sufficient numbers to become established.

The Ring-necked Parakeets breeding ferally in various places in western Europe and the Middle East may be the result of escapes or deliberate releases, or both, but the Little Owls of Britain are all descended from stock intentionally introduced in the nineteenth century by landowning bird-lovers. This was but one among many attempts to establish in Britain a range of more exotic birds, from Purple Swamphens to Pekin Robins. King Penguins were also released in north Norway in 1936, odd ones surviving to the late 1940s.

Extinctions

The Palearctic has lost few species in the last 400 years. Many have declined alarmingly, and some have now gone from individual countries or areas, but

the only certain total extinctions in the region since 1600 are a handful of island birds.

Most famous were the Great Auks that formerly nested in north Scotland (St Kilda, probably Orkney), the Faeroes, Iceland and possibly Greenland, as well as Newfoundland (*p.26*), entirely on offshore islands and stacks. About five times as heavy as Common Guillemots and flightless, they were easy prey to fishermen; the last two were killed on Eldey, Iceland, in June 1844. At the other end of the Palearctic, another seabird that did not survive much longer was Pallas's Cormorant, of Ostrov Beringa between Kamchatka and the Aleutians; it was wiped out in about 1852.

The Canarian Black Oystercatcher is thought to have been extinct since 1913, though there have been odd reports in the past 25 years.

All the remaining extinctions relate to Japanese islands. Indeed, with the Nansei-shotō (Ryūkyū Islands) left to the Indomalayan region, the only other certain extinctions since 1600 relate to Ogasawara-shotō (Bonin Islands). There the nineteenth century saw the end of Kittlitz's Thrush (1828), Kittlitz's Pigeon (1889) and the Ogasawara Grosbeak (1890).

One renowned continental 'is-it-or-is-it-not-extinct' is the Crested Shelduck of eastern Asia. This mainly grey and black shelduck has been recorded only three times in the past half century – in 1943, 1964 and 1971 – always in what would be winter quarters between Vladivostok and South Korea. Access is difficult in the border regions of Russia, China and North Korea and so the fact that each sighting involved more than one bird (six in 1971) has kept alive a lingering hope. Then in 1990 came reports, not yet confirmed, of a small population in quite a different part of China, north-east Yunnan.

Threatened birds

There may have been few extinctions, but over 80 Palearctic birds – around 7 per cent of the total and almost four times as many as in the Nearctic – give cause for concern. Many are large and mainly migra-

tory species of wetlands. They include the Dalmatian Pelican (**25**), Swinhoe's Egret (**26**), Oriental White Stork, Crested Ibis (**27**), Northern Bald Ibis (**28**) and a whole series of cranes – Black-necked, Hooded, White-naped (*see title page*), Siberian White (**29**), and Red-crowned (**30**) – all of which are classed as 'Endangered', or at least 'Vulnerable' or 'Rare'.

Drainage, shooting and pollution appear to have reduced the total numbers of the Oriental White Stork, of north-east Asia, to two or three thousand at most. This decrease is paralleled, though not yet as seriously, by the smaller White Stork of Europe. Long linked with good luck and fecundity – though, sadly, its decline is not having any noticeable effect on human populations – it is becoming ever scarcer in at least its western range, perhaps mainly through intensive farming, including the use of pesticides; the plethora of power lines is another modern hazard for large birds. White Storks are also shot (like many other birds) on migration through notorious sections of the Mediterranean and, perhaps more seriously, are suffering both from pesticides and from the successful control of locusts (an important winter food) in Africa.

Other water-associated species giving cause for concern include the Pygmy Cormorant of south-east Europe to the Aral Sea (drainage); the Japanese Night-heron, which winters south to the Philippines (deforestation and drainage); and, in particular, the Black-faced Spoonbill of North Korea and east China (drainage and disturbance).

Among wildfowl in the same boat are the Lesser White-fronted Goose of arctic Eurasia (general decline over half a century); the Baykal Teal of eastern Siberia (excessive hunting in winter quarters in Japan and China at least contributing); the Marbled Duck, patchily distributed from Iberia and Morocco to Turkestan and Afghanistan (long decline of a relict species, but some recent increase in the west); the Scaly-sided Merganser (**31**); the White-headed Duck of Iberia and north-west Africa to north-west China (drainage, habitat loss and relict distribution, but some recovery in Spain with protection); and the Mandarin Duck of China to Japan (deforestation and captive exports). In the last connection, feral Mandarins in southern England now represent some 10–15 per cent of the world total.

The pheasants, so typical of eastern Asia, and partridges are another family with a number of threatened Palearctic species. Those classed as 'Endangered' include the Chinese Monal (32) and the Brown Eared Pheasant (see 66). Other Chinese gamebirds now of uncertain status include Reeves's, Lady Amherst's and Blue Eared Pheasants and the Sichuan Partridge.

The Altai Snowcock, one of the five large greyish snowcocks of Eurasian mountains above 2500 m, is also little known in its range on the borders of China, Mongolia and Russia. Another mountain plant-eater, the Caucasian Black Grouse, is vulnerable to competition from grazing sheep, as well as to disturbance by shepherds' dogs; hunting and, in some parts, deforestation may also be affecting this smaller and longer-tailed cousin of the Common Black Grouse.

Many birds of prey, particularly vultures and fish-eagles which are highly susceptible to poisoned carcases, have long declined throughout much of their Palearctic ranges. Vultures have, in general, decreased drastically and the largest of them, the Cinereous, now has only a few hundred pairs in the whole of Europe and an increasingly fragmented range in central Asia.

White-tailed Fish-eagles (33), although perhaps still reasonably numerous in northern Eurasia, have seriously decreased in the southern parts of their range from Germany and the Balkans to Manchuria, as well as in Greenland. Pallas's Fish-eagles, of central and southern Asia, have all but gone from the former USSR. On the other hand, Steller's Fish-eagles, which breed on Asia's vast eastern peninsula of Kamchatka, are – to judge from the numbers now found wintering in Japan – less at risk than might have been thought.

Three other birds of prey are worth special mention here. The Imperial Eagle, although found from Spain to central Asia, has decreased almost everywhere –

mainly through shooting, pesticides, kinds of habitat destruction (it nests largely in trees) and other forms of disturbance – so that the world population is thought to be well under 10,000; the distinctive Spanish race (34) is particularly 'Endangered'.

Red Kites are exclusively western Palearctic, and chiefly European. There are now probably not much more than 25,000 adults, mainly in Spain, France and Germany, and they are still threatened by poisoned baits – to which they too are particularly vulnerable – as well as by trapping, shooting and other such senseless irritations as egg-collecting. Common even in London until the 1500s, Red Kites were persecuted almost to extinction throughout Britain in the eighteenth and nineteenth centuries; only about a dozen remained in mid Wales. They are still among Britain's rarer raptors, but intensive protection has raised the breeding population more than tenfold to over 120.

The raptor with the widest world distribution of all, the Peregrine Falcon (pp.15, 28), has more than recovered its numbers in Britain and Ireland after the pesticide crash of the 1950s, but continues to cause concern in some continental European countires.

Seabird populations have been seriously affected at local levels in many areas through human overfishing, oil disasters and other pollution, but vast numbers of petrels, shearwaters, gannets, skuas, gulls, terns and auks still breed in the Palearctic. The species at risk are threatened primarily because of now limited ranges and relatively small numbers. Japanese Murrelets, for example, are small auks that breed only on Izu-shotō, islands south of Tokyo, where they appear to be under some threat from disturbance.

The Short-tailed Albatross, the largest and only white-bodied albatross of the three that breed in the north Pacific (chapter 8), was once widespread in several island groups from the Taiwan Strait to Ogasawara-gunto nearly 2500 km away to the south of Japan, but then was almost exterminated by Japanese plume-hunters in the late nineteenth and early twentieth centuries. Now there are only about 250 in what may be the sole colony, on Tori-shima, and even that has been achieved only by protection: in the early 1950s a mere half-a-dozen pairs remained.

Soft-plumaged Petrels breed on various islands in the southern oceans and, quite separately, in the Madeira and Cape Verde groups, where two distinct races are involved. The subspecies on Madeira itself is classed as 'Endangered', that on outlying islets and the Cape Verdes as 'Rare'. These birds are taken for food on the Cape Verdes, and both populations suffer the depredations of rats and other introduced mammals.

Four gulls and a tern are also causing concern because of limited ranges and small numbers. Audouin's Gull breeds only in the Mediterranean area, with a population of, perhaps, under 8000 pairs. The White-eyed Gull is endemic to the Red Sea and the Gulf of Aden. Both are at risk from disturbance, pollution and oil slicks. In central Asia the appropriately named Relict Gull has a disjointed breeding range between Balkhash and Baykal; there may be only a couple of thousand pairs and it is certainly 'Rare'. Another dark-headed species, Saunders's Gull, nests in northern China, mainly inland, and winters on the coasts of China and Korea; it is evidently nowhere as successful as some of the other smaller gulls with black or brown hoods. The Chinese Crested Tern is even less well-known, so much so that it is at best rare, at worst extinct; it may breed on islands off Shandong and may winter south to Thailand, the Philippines and even Bali, but nothing is sure.

The bustards are an Old World family that has suffered greatly in the twentieth century from the spread of marginal agriculture by an ever increasing human population (*p.13*) and from excessive shooting. None has suffered more from hunting than the Houbara. This sandy-buff and white bustard, with a frill of black and white feathers down the neck, lives in semideserts and steppes from the Canaries and north-west Africa to Mongolia; it walks (with a mincing gait) or runs rather than flies when threatened, or crouches flat in an attempt to avoid detection. Houbara Bustards

32
CHINESE MONAL PHEASANT
Lophophorus lhuysii

The Common Pheasant has been introduced, cosseted and shot at in many parts of the world, but pheasants as a group are in a parlous state: half the 48 species – all but one Asiatic – are at risk; some are endangered. Rarest of three big, stout, short-tailed monal pheasants, this bird lives above the tree-line in west China, coming below 3000 m only in winter. It has long been near extinction, probably through excessive hunting in its small upland scrub range. The male, with bare blue eye-patches and bushy green crest, is iridescent purple, blue and copper above, except for a white lower back, and black below glossed purple and green on the throat; the dark female has a white back too.

33

WHITE-TAILED FISH-EAGLE
Haliaeetus albicilla

Fish-eagles are big and bulky with long broad wings, strong bills and feet, and no close kinship to the true eagles. Most eat fish, aquatic birds and mammals, and carrion. North America's Bald Eagle is one of the ten species. The White-tailed, spanning up to 2·4 m, has – like some others – suffered badly from the shooting and poisoning long accorded to birds of prey, more recently from pesticides, pollution, and deforestation of its wetland habitats. There may still be well over 10,000 from Greenland to Japan, but in many areas the numbers are but a fraction of what they were. Reintroduction attempts in Scotland, where they became extinct in 1916, appear to be proving successful.

have long been prime targets for Arab falconers and, in the past half century, for gun-happy 'sportsmen' using automatic weapons from vehicles. Everywhere their numbers have been much reduced, by over 75 per cent in some areas. The central Asiatic population is migratory, wintering from the Persian Gulf to Pakistan and so also falling foul of the hunters.

There are still probably many thousands of Great Bustards from Iberia to China, but their range has become fragmented and their numbers also reduced by conversion of grassland to agriculture, and by mechanised farming, hunting and possibly pesticides. (These bulky birds – the males weighing up to 18 kg – once ranged over much of England; there has been a long-running attempt to reintroduce them to Salisbury Plain.) The far smaller Little Bustards of western and southern Europe and west-central Asia are also increasingly at risk from similar threats.

The two-note rasping call of the Corn Crake is heard less and less in Britain and, while decreases elsewhere in its considerable Eurasian range are not yet so marked, this is another whose future needs to be watched. The little-known Swinhoe's Yellow Crake, which breeds in eastern Siberia and Manchuria, is apparently very scarce in its winter quarters in eastern China, Korea and Japan.

The Sociable Plover – so called because it often breeds in loose groups of up to 25 pairs, though it is otherwise less gregarious than some plovers – nests in central Asia and winters south to north-east Africa and north-west India; it nests on scrubby steppe and it too is decreasing with the spread of cultivation. Other much rarer eastern waders include the Spotted Greenshank (**35**) and the tiny Spoon-billed Sandpiper, generally rather like a stint but for its extraordinary beak. The Spoon-billed Sandpiper breeds in far north-eastern Asia and winters from south-east India to southern China, but its total population is probably no more than a few thousands.

Old breeding records exist of the Whimbrel-sized Slender-billed Curlew around the Ob and Irtysh

valleys, but the species has greatly declined in the past 100 years and nobody now knows where in western Siberia the small numbers that winter in coastal north-west Africa come from. Travelling in the opposite direction, to winter in south-east Asia, Indonesia and even Australia, the Asiatic Dowitcher is another wader that is relatively little known but evidently rare, even though occasional winter flocks of some hundreds have been seen.

A number of landbirds endemic to islands are at risk because of their restricted ranges. Three Atlantic pigeons – the Long-toed of Madeira and the Laurel and Bolle's of the Canary Islands – were all reduced in numbers by hunting and by destruction of their specialised laurel and tree-heath habitats. All three are classed as 'Rare', as, also in the Canaries, are the Blue Chaffinch of Gran Canaria and Tenerife and the Fuerteventura Stonechat. The once common Raso

34
SPANISH IMPERIAL EAGLE
Aquila heliaca adalberti

Imperial Eagles, with a wing-span often over 2 m, are patchily distributed from Iberia to central Asia, mainly in grassy lowlands with scattered trees. There are probably only a few thousands in all, and in Europe just a few hundreds. The isolated Spanish race, sometimes thought a distinct species, numbers fewer than 100 and is seriously endangered. This large dark eagle has the same cream to buff crown, white 'braces' and grey-based tail as other Imperials, but also white shoulders. It feeds on rabbits and hares, some other mammals and birds and, in winter, carrion. It has lost much habitat to cultivation and suffers from persecution, poisoning and pesticides.

35

SPOTTED GREENSHANK

Tringa guttifer

This wader is smaller – and far rarer – than the
Greenshank of Eurasia that winters widely from
Africa to Australia. The Spotted Greenshank is
only known to nest on Sakhalin Island, north of
Japan, but – shy and easily overlooked – it may do so
on the adjacent Russian mainland too. It winters in
Bangladesh and Thailand. The yellowish legs are
only three-fifths as long as a Greenshank's, with
curious partially webbed toes, and the straighter bill
is yellow-green at the base; in summer there are many
more and larger black spots on the underbody. It
does not breed on the ground as most waders do;
instead, like Green and Solitary Sandpipers, it uses
the old tree nest of some other bird.

Lark, endemic to the tiny island of that name in the Cape Verdes, has recently fluctuated between about 20 and a hundred or two and is classed as 'Endangered'.

Two local western Palearctic nuthatches appear on lists of birds at risk, but the Corsican Nuthatch has a thriving population in old pine forests that are not threatened; and the Algerian Nuthatch, though originally classed as 'Rare' when it was known only from the single mountain where it was first discovered in the early 1970s, has now been found in three more places. At the other end of the Palearctic, the Japanese Yellow Bunting is a rare endemic of the uplands of central Honshu.

Several more Palearctic landbirds with question marks over their status are little known rather than necessarily threatened or even rare. Many are largely or entirely in poorly studied areas of China, such as Vaurie's Nightjar (discovered only in 1960), the Rufous-headed and Black-throated Robins, the Omei Liocichla (a babbler), Heude's Eye-browed Parrotbill, the Speckled Reed and Japanese Marsh Warblers, Jankowski's Bunting and the Sichuan Jay. Some may be threatened by deforestation, drainage or other habitat destruction; others simply have tiny ranges.

Red-necked Nightjars, endemic to Iberia and north-west Africa, are still common enough in Spain, but probably declining in the Maghreb as a whole and vulnerable to disturbance and destruction of their scrub and open woodland habitats. The migratory Yellow-eyed Pigeon of central Asia is becoming rarer in its winter quarters in Pakistan and north-west India. And Blakiston's Fish-owl of east Siberia to north Japan is generally scarce with its special habitat requirement of ice-free rivers.

Sub-Saharan Africa and south Arabia

Perhaps surprisingly, the Afrotropical region boasts little more than half as many bird species as the Neotropical (*chapter 2*). Including regular migrants – but not vagrants – the total for South America alone is over 2900, compared with about 1800 for the whole of Africa. This is despite the continent of Africa's being, at 30·3 million square km, not so far short of twice the size of South America.

Until Abyssinia became Ethiopia, the Afrotropics were known as the Ethiopian region: the Greek *aithiops* ('burnt face') applied to all the African countries inhabited by Negro and other dark-skinned races. Theoretically, the region takes in those parts of Africa and Arabia that lie south of the Tropic of Cancer, but the northern boundary is not as clear as that. The Sahara and Arabian desert areas are somewhat transitional between the Afrotropical and Palearctic regions, with their own restricted and rather specialised faunas.

For ornithological purposes, the Afrotropical region is now generally taken to include the Sahel savannah and the Aïr and Ennedi massifs, but not the open desert. Thus, the southern half of Mauritania, the major parts of Mali, Niger and Chad, and all of Sudan fall inside. In Saudi Arabia the boundary now tends to be pushed farther north, to the line of 28°N (roughly, the mouth of the Gulf of Aqaba): south-west Arabia has about ten endemic species, and breeding outposts of four times as many of what are otherwise essentially African birds.

The region takes in all inshore islands, such as those in the Gulf of Guinea and off the coasts of Tanzania and Arabia, but not the Cape Verdes (*chapter 3*) or

Madagascar and the Comoros (*chapter 5*). It is also convenient to include here the South Atlantic islands of Ascension, St Helena, Tristan da Cunha and Gough.

Thus, the whole lies largely within the tropics, except for the north-central section of Saudi Arabia and, in the south, much of South Africa and southern Namibia, Botswana and Mozambique, together with Tristan and Gough.

Africa as a continent is second only to Asia in size. With the Palearctic part deleted and southern Arabia added, the area of the Afrotropical region is reduced to 26·5 million square km. Roughly 25 per cent is desert and subdesert, including much of the Arabian peninsula, the Sahel and southern edge of the Sahara, the Sudanian plain, the Danakil and Ogaden in north-east Africa, the area around Lake Turkana in Kenya, and the Namib and Kalahari in the south-west. About 15 per cent is grassland with acacia and other thornscrub, and nearly 35 per cent various kinds of broadleaved woodlands and savannahs. Another 5 per cent is a mixture of riverine gallery forest and wooded ridges. Less than 10 per cent is rainforest.

The lowland forests are centred on Zaïre, Congo and Gabon, and extend in a relatively narrow and steadily diminishing strip along the Gulf of Guinea to Sierra Leone. More isolated pockets of lowland forest are also found in northern Angola and near the coast of Kenya and Tanzania. Some of the montane regions from south-west Arabia and Ethiopia down the Rift Valley and, in smaller areas, farther south, as well as in Cameroon and Angola, are also forested and no less threatened by Man's activities. To the north and south of the forest zone are wide belts of broadleaved woodland and savannah, giving way to steppe and thornbush, and then to desert and subdesert.

The Rift, running 10,000 km from the Middle East to Mozambique, includes a whole series of bird-rich freshwater and alkaline lakes. And between its east African arms lies Lake Victoria, second only in size to North America's Lake Superior among the world's largest fresh waters. The river systems of the Nile, Zaïre and Niger are three of the world's top 15, all over 4000 km in length. Apart from a couple of outcrops in the west, all the real uplands are in the east and south, from Ethiopia down to South Africa. There the montane zones are extensive, particularly the Ethiopian highlands split by the Rift Valley, but only three peaks in all Africa – Kilimanjaro, Kirinyaga (Mount Kenya) and Mount Stanley – exceed 5000 m. These highlands hold many remarkable endemic Afro-alpine plants, several of which, such as the giant lobelias and groundsels, exhibit gigantism; the same highlands hold a number of endemic birds.

Indigenous birds

Including southern Arabia and various islands – but not Madagascar (*chapter 5*) – the Afrotropical region has just over 1750 indigenous breeding species, a total that is increased to 1900 by the inclusion of the regular migrants. The corresponding Neotropical figures are about 3425 and nearly 3600; indeed, that African 1900 is only 12 per cent more than the list for the South American country of Colombia alone.

This Afrotropical region covers between one-fifth and one-sixth of the world's landmass, and between one-fifth and one-sixth of all bird species live there. Thus, its avifauna might be thought 'about average', but anyone who goes to sub-Saharan Africa quickly has a different impression. A good many of the birds are common and very visible, having generally had less persecution, at least in the tropics, than in many parts of the world.

And both the species total and especially the numbers in the Sahel savannah and other parts of tropical Africa are increased in the northern winter by hundreds of millions of Palearctic migrants of nearly 190 species (150 of which do not otherwise occur there): these include storks, raptors, terns, doves, cuckoos, nightjars, swifts, bee-eaters, rollers, and, especially, ducks and waders, as well as the vast hordes of such passerines as swallows, pipits, chats, flycatchers, warblers, shrikes and orioles. In some areas the migrants can greatly outnumber the residents. In the African continent as a whole, however, it has been estimated that there may be at least 70,000 million residents, compared with less than 5000 million Palearctic migrants.

Among residents, a number of cosmopolitan groupings – ducks, rails, cuckoos, owls, swifts and kingfishers – are all represented by between one-fifth and one-sixth of the world's species, again appropriate to the size of the landmass. But the region holds higher proportions of some other widespread families: one-quarter of the cranes and nightjars; one-third of the herons and storks and nearly the same proportion of the ibises and spoonbills. Among some of the world's larger families, the Afrotropical region has over a quarter of the 120 or so true finches (but only 5 per cent of the 280-odd buntings); around a third of the 325 thrushes (mainly smaller chats); half of the 80 swallows; and four-fifths of the 75 shrikes, including all the bush-shrikes. It also has ten of the 46 tits (and seven of the ten penduline tits).

On the other hand, while pigeons and doves seem everywhere in Africa, the region actually has little more than one-ninth of the world's 300 species. Woodpeckers, too, are not uncommon but under-represented, with less than one-eighth of the world's 200. And the region holds just nine of the 113 crows. Partridges, notably francolins (*see* **44**), are plentiful but there are few quails and only one pheasant, the remarkable African Peafowl (*see* **43**); against that, all but one of the half-dozen guineafowls, which, as a group, are believed to have originated in Asia, are now exclusively Afrotropical.

Some proportions of shared birds are very different from those in the other tropical regions. In contrast to the single species in the Americas, more than two-thirds of the world's 86 larks occur within the Afrotropics and the transitional Saharan and Arabian zones. Similarly, nearly half of the 59 wagtails, pipits and longclaws breed in the Afrotropical region – four times as many as in the Neotropics.

Three large but loose cosmopolitan groupings are the diurnal raptors, waders, and seabirds. Diurnal raptors – especially kites, Old World vultures and various genera of eagles – are often common in the Afrotropical region, where this group is represented by almost 70 breeding species, nearly a quarter of the world's total; over 20 more are Palearctic migrants.

Waders are unevenly represented. The small families of jacanas, painted-snipes, oystercatchers, and avocets and stilts all have one or two species each in Africa. More significantly, the region holds more than one-quarter of the world's plovers (including half of the lapwings), one-third of the thick-knees, and over half of the coursers and pratincoles. On the other hand, the largest wader family, including all the 'sandpipers' – a world total of almost 90 species – is represented among breeding birds only by the African Snipe (though, of course, many others come down to Africa in vast numbers for the northern winter).

In general, too, seabirds have a poor diversity of breeding species in most of the Afrotropics. Apart from cormorants, terns and certain gulls, not many true seabirds nest in Africa, southern Arabia or their inshore islands, though various albatrosses, petrels, shearwaters, frigatebirds and skuas are regular visitors in the non-breeding seasons. Two tropicbirds, two boobies and probably one shearwater breed on islets in the Red Sea and Arabian area, and one or two also in the Gulf of Guinea; one penguin and one gannet nest on inshore islands along the Namibian and South African coasts (along with five cormorants and several gulls and terns).

36

NEWTON'S FISCAL SHRIKE
Lanius newtoni

Unlike the bush-shrikes (41), the typical shrikes perch on conspicuous vantage-points from which they hunt their prey. Few do so more openly than the half-dozen African fiscal shrikes – named for their smart 'legal' dress of black or grey above and white below. Most are common enough in bushy grassland, one associated with watersides, another with subdesert. But, though often considered a race of the common Fiscal of much of sub-Saharan Africa, Newton's Fiscal is a rare bird of deep rainforest on São Tomé. This equatorial island in the Gulf of Guinea, 50 by 25 km, is under 300 km offshore, but has no fewer than 17 endemic birds: a dozen full species, the rest races of mainland forms.

But the seabird total goes up considerably with the inclusion of the four South Atlantic archipelagos. The breeding birds there add another penguin, three albatrosses, eight petrels and shearwaters, four storm-petrels, one diving-petrel, two tropicbirds, three boobies, one frigatebird, one skua, and half-a-dozen terns. Of these, the Atlantic Petrel and the Ascension Frigatebird are endemic.

All the families and other groupings so far considered are widely distributed in the world. Essentially Old World groups for which the Afrotropical region is particularly important include three-quarters of the bustards, two-thirds of the colourful bee-eaters, and over half of the rollers (as well as the single widely represented hoopoe).

And, among the more numerous Old World passerines, the region holds around a third of the 26 orioles, 106 starlings, and 108 flycatchers; over two-fifths of the 120 bulbuls and 350 warblers (including all but three of the 45 cisticolas, or grass-warblers); more than half of over 40 sparrows and sparrow-weavers, and no fewer than 92 of 105 typical weavers; well over half of more than 130 estrildid finches; and nearly two-thirds of 120 sunbirds. Most of the rest of the sunbirds, and of several others of these families, are Indomalayan.

Among circumglobal tropical families, parrots (only 19 of over 340 species) and trogons (only three of almost 40) are not well represented, but over half the world's barbets are African (now proposed as a separate family), as are two each of the seven pelicans and five flamingos (one in huge numbers). Like the other tropical regions, Africa holds one darter, one finfoot, and one skimmer.

Turning to strictly Old World families that are mainly tropical, the buttonquails, the pittas (only two of nearly 30) and the drongos (only three of over 20) all have a poor showing. And Africa holds less than one-sixth of the nearly 80 cuckoo-shrikes; only one-eighth of the 255 babblers; and a mere nine of the 90-odd white-eyes. Moreover, while certain white-eyes are common in continental Africa, several of the nine are confined to inshore islands: in fact, a high proportion of the world's white-eyes are endemic to islands (*chapters 5 and 8*). On the credit side of mainly tropical Old World families, ten of the 16 sandgrouse, half of the 48 hornbills, four of the 14 broadbills, and all but two of the 17 honeyguides live in the Afrotropics.

Whereas one-third of all Neotropical bird families (and half of the resident families) are confined to that region, only ten of Africa's 90 or so traditional families are endemic. Four of these involve single species: the familiar Ostrich (which formerly extended into Palearctic Africa and may still penetrate central Mauritania); the Hamerkop (an aberrant brown heron-stork with short legs and a hammer-shaped head of longish bill and protruding crest); the Shoebill (another heron-stork, standing well over a metre high, grey with an enormous hooked and boat-shaped beak); and the Secretarybird (a terrestrial and somewhat stork-like raptor with a bunch of quill-pens on its head). The others are the 22 turacos (*see* **40**); the half-dozen mousebirds (small-bodied, long-tailed, grey-brown and gregarious); the half-dozen or more wood-hoopoes (also long-tailed and mostly gregarious, but

37
NDUK EAGLE-OWL
Bubo vosseleri

Among the 15 or so eagle-owls, half of them African, some are 70 cm or more in length. The rare Nduk Eagle-owl, restricted to the highland forests of the Usambaras in north-east Tanzania, is only three-quarters of that size. It is often treated as a race of the still smaller Fraser's Eagle-owl of West and Central Africa, but the two are long isolated by nearly 1000 km and, importantly, have different calls. The Nduk is tawny above, whitish below, blotched and barred, with obvious ear-tufts like most eagle-owls, but browner eyes, not yellow or red. Long known from only a few old specimens, it is now realised to have a population of several hundreds, but forest clearance threatens.

largely black and often glossed green, purple or blue with red to yellow bills); the two sugarbirds (dull brown with decurved beaks and, especially on the males, long tails); the nine helmet-shrikes (variably patterned, mostly with forward-projecting feathers on the forehead, and again notably gregarious); and the 14 parasitic whydahs (stumpy and streaky, but the males mostly developing complicated plumages and long tails for breeding).

Five further subfamilies (a taxonomic nicety) might also be treated as endemic: the six guineafowls and the 47 bush-shrikes (though one of each actually just extends into North Africa); the two picathartes (*see* **39**); the three buffalo-weavers; and the two oxpeckers, or tickbirds. The last are a particularly interesting endemic subfamily of starlings, which have evolved in association with Africa's wide range of hoofed mammals and which have stiff tails for support (like woodpeckers) and specially adapted short legs for clinging to, and walking and hopping about on, often vertical parts of furred or bare flesh.

A number of families, such as the crab-plovers, sandgrouse, honeyguides, broadbills and bulbuls, are

38
WESTERN WATTLED CUCKOO-SHRIKE
Campephaga lobata

*Only 11 of the large tropical family of cuckoo-shrikes (**59**) live in Africa; with such limited competition, most have wide ranges. Confined to the fragmented Guinea forests of Liberia and Ghana, however, this one is rare and endangered. Quite small, under 20 cm long, the male has glossy dark blue-green head, yellow-green back, green-edged black wings, yellow-tipped black and greenish tail, and rufous rump and underbody. The related Eastern Wattled, of Cameroon to Zaïre, has rump and underparts yellow. Both are named for the big fleshy yellow to orange wattles under dark red eyes (other male African cuckoo-shrikes have less obvious gape-wattles). The females are duller and yellower.*

shared only with the Indomalayan region or, in a few cases, also the extreme south Palearctic. Indeed, shared families in general have as much to do with the Indomalayan region as with the adjacent Palearctic. This applies even more to shared breeding species, most of which are larger non-passerines. Often, too, the Arabian peninsula is a sort of meeting ground with the Indomalayan region: for example, the Indian Silverbill, an estrildid finch, nests in east Arabia, and the African Silverbill in south-west Arabia.

Nearly 160 breeding species are shared with the Palearctic. Palearctic families missing from the continental Afrotropics and not even occurring here in the northern winters include the divers, auks, dippers, wrens, long-tailed tits, nuthatches, wallcreepers, treecreepers and, but for an isolated species in the Yemen, the accentors. As we have seen, too, petrels and skuas – well represented in the Palearctic – here nest only on

39
WHITE-NECKED PICATHARTES
Picathartes gymnocephalus

The two strange picathartes, also known as 'bare-headed rockfowl' or 'bald crows', are primitive insect-eaters in a family of their own. Some 30–35 cm in length, with crow-like bills and long necks and tails, they hop along the ground on heavy-toed longish legs. Where this species is white below, with orange head and black 'ear-muffs', the Grey-necked has greyer throat, orange underbody, and blue and red head with black sides. Both live in Guinea rainforests, this one from Sierra Leone to Togo, the other from eastern Nigeria to Gabon; little colonies build cup-nests of mud on rock faces. Deforestation menaces; White-necked are also too often captured for a short life in a zoo.

40

THE ENDEMIC TURACOS OF AFRICA,
AND BANNERMAN'S TURACO
Tauraco bannermani

Africa, like other tropical regions, has many colourful birds, but the turacos are as striking as any. This essentially Afrotropical family also epitomises that continent's avifauna by its division into forest and savannah groups. Three-quarters of the 22 species are predominantly glossy green, violet or blue, all but one with large red patches on the open wings; these are relatively shy forest or woodland birds. The other five are mainly grey, several with plain or streaked white bellies, and one a white chest and bare black face; still impressive, and much more obvious in rather open country and dry bush, these are usually known as plantain-eaters or go-away-birds.

The latter name is simply onomatopoeic, from characteristic calls. On the other hand, 'plantain-eater' is, confusingly, the literal meaning of the Latinised word *Musophaga* which is applied not to any of these grey species but to the violet turacos. Furthermore, although all the family feeds mainly on figs and other fruits – as well as on leaves, buds and flowers – none actually eats plantains, which in this context are bananas.

Most are 35–50 cm long, except for the Great Blue Turaco which is half as big again as the largest of the rest: all grey-blue above, with a blackish crest and tail-band, it is blue-green shading into yellow and chestnut below. The Violet and Ross's Turacos are entirely violet-black and purple, with either a red crown or a red crest. These two have mainly red or crimson flight-feathers, concealed when the wings are folded, as do all the green group which also have many other colours in their plumages.

Turacos have crests of various shapes and sizes. Some simply give the head a large or domed appearance, but others are peaked, pointed or upstanding. The predominantly grey plantain-eaters and go-away-birds also have obvious crests, extending up or back from the forecrown or, in two cases, giving a shaggy back to the head. The bills of most turacos are relatively small and may be red, yellow or black. But those of the blue, violet and grey groups are large, showy, and usually yellow.

All turacos are essentially arboreal, loping and hopping along or between branches. They fly as little as possible, mainly from tree to tree, with ungainly flaps and glides. This seems rather a waste of those bright red wings, but that colour is used in displays, which include bowing the head and flashing the wings and tail.

Turacos are often in pairs or small parties, and noisy with choruses of hoarse grunts, barks and coos. Perhaps rather unexpectedly, they build flat pigeon-like nests of twigs, sometimes rather flimsy, in trees or tall bushes. Again like pigeons, most species lay only two eggs. The young start to clamber about on the branches after about three weeks, well before they can fly.

Some turacos have extensive ranges and most are not as yet threatened. But they are commonly taken as cagebirds and, as the forests decrease, there is a risk of overexploitation, in the same way as has already happened with so many parrots (**23**). Even a few turacos of restricted distribution – such as Fischer's Turaco, mainly green with red bill, eye-patches and nape, in the coastal woodlands of East

Africa, and the green, blue and purple Ruwenzori Turaco of the mountains to the west of Lake Victoria – are at present locally common or even numerous.

On the other hand, Ruspoli's Turaco – characterised by its bushy grey-cream crest – is confined to a few small areas in southern Ethiopia, and relatively rare; while Bannerman's Turaco, illustrated here, is already classed as 'Endangered'. Named after David Bannerman, one of the pioneers in the study of West African birds, this species is confined to one small region of mountain forest at 1800–2500 m in the Bamenda-Banso highlands of west Cameroon. The population in Oku (now Kilum) Forest is considered crucial to its survival; since 1986 this forest has been the subject of an intensive ICBP conservation programme.

Bannerman's Turaco has many of the colours that are typical of the forest species, being green to golden-green with a greyer belly and a mainly blue-black tail, as well as the usual red patches in the wings which produces a vivid visual explosion in flight, but additionally it has a crimson crown and crest. These it shares with the related Red-crested Turaco of northern Angola, 1500 km to the south. Indeed, the Red-crested is very similar, but for its white (not grey) cheeks and its smaller and differently structured yellow bill without any reddish on top.

oceanic islands, though they and other seabirds are found in Afrotropical waters during the northern and antarctic winters.

Nearly 1550 of the 1750 Afrotropical species are endemic, particularly in south-west Arabia, Somalia, the Ethiopian highlands, the East African highlands, the forests of Zaïre and Angola, the mountains of Cameroon, the deserts of Namibia, and the islands in the Gulf of Guinea and South Atlantic. It is some of these that are most endangered.

Introductions

Introduced birds play a rather insignificant part in the Afrotropical region. Common Mynahs, Common Starlings and House Sparrows have inevitably been brought in, particularly to South Africa and to port areas and islands elsewhere. Equally inevitably, they have prospered locally: the sparrow is now widespread in South Africa and the two starlings, despite more competitors, also have fair ranges there. Common Mynahs, too, are naturalised in various places around the Red Sea and Persian Gulf, while on St Helena, in the South Atlantic, they are now common enough to be a threat to some indigenous species.

Other birds more locally established in South Africa include Mute Swans and Chukar Partridges, but the attempts of early settlers to naturalise familiar song-birds were far less successful than in New Zealand (*chapter 7*): only the Common Chaffinch, introduced to the Cape by Cecil Rhodes in 1898, is well established and even that has not spread far. Various parrots, such as Ring-necked Parakeets and one or two lovebirds, have also been translocated in Africa, probably through escapes. Similarly, Red Avadavats (from India eastwards) and Rüppell's Weavers (from Africa) breed ferally around Ar Riyad in Saudi Arabia.

Introductions of birds to continental landmasses are often unsuccessful unless the species is particularly aggressive or adaptable. If successful, in contrast to what happens on small islands, they may still have little impact on firmly established competitors. But the

House Crow, of India, was introduced to Zanzibar in the 1890s, and in the last 50 years has spread from there to Dar es Salaam, Mombasa and elsewhere. Probably shipborne, it has even appeared in Seychelles (*see chapter 5*), down the Indian Ocean to Durban and up the Red Sea to Aqaba since the 1970s, as well as in the

41
GREEN-BREASTED BUSH-SHRIKE
Malaconotus gladiator

The bush-shrikes are an African group of over 45 species (one reaches Arabia). They differ in various ways from the typical shrikes: in particular, most are colourful and – though noisy – shy and secretive. Some live in dry bush or savannah, others in wetland thickets or overgrown gardens. This Green-breasted is a forest bird that, rare and known only from the highlands of west Cameroon and adjacent Nigeria, must be threatened by felling. It is closely related to the widespread Grey-headed, which is similarly coloured but with white in front of the eyes and all yellow to orange below. Both are over 25 cm long, with massive beaks and fierce looks, but bush-shrikes eat mainly insects.

Persian Gulf as far north as Kuwait. Wherever it becomes established, it tends to displace any competitors (for example, the Pied Crow in East Africa) and, locally at least, can have a serious impact on the populations of small birds.

Extinctions

It is not certain that any African bird has become extinct in the past 400 years, though one or two have not been seen for a long time. Other species have very few records, but local or rare forest birds can be difficult to find and even some more open habitats are still poorly researched. Thus, two lost forest weavers of Zaïre recently 'reappeared' after several decades (*p.89*) and the Yellow-throated Serin, of highland Ethiopia, after more than a century (*p.94*).

Similarly, three of the distinctive birds of the Gulf of Guinea islands were not seen for 50 years or more, but then relocated by thorough research during 1988–91. All on São Tomé, these are the Dwarf Ibis, usually treated as a race of Africa's Olive Ibis; Newton's Fiscal Shrike (36); and the São Tomé Grosbeak.

The only two certain extinctions since 1600 in the whole Afrotropical region as defined here have been on South Atlantic islands: the Ascension Flightless Rail (about 1656) and the Tristan Moorhen (late nineteenth century). But these losses had more to do with the problems facing island birds (*chapters 2, 5 and 8*) than with the Afrotropics. Indeed, other species disappeared quite quickly after the South Atlantic islands were discovered by Europeans in the early 1500s. St Helena lost all but one of its indigenous landbirds before 1600: for example, the Crumby Cuckoo and the flightless Giant Hoopoe were both extinct fairly soon after the island was first visited in 1502.

Threatened birds

The past 40 years have actually seen the discovery of more new African species – over two dozen at the very least – than extinctions of birds in the world as a whole. The number of ornithologists now researching African birds in field or museum will doubtless, as in other tropical regions, continue to throw up new endemics of restricted range.

Most of these relatively recent new species are small songbirds, but they include a honeyguide, a tinkerbird, a swift and two owls. Some are known only from one or two museum specimens. Several are simply hard to identify, or live in remote areas; others are rare, secretive and restricted in range. Since almost nothing is known about them, it is difficult to say how threatened they may be, but several are apparently endemic to areas where their particular habitats are under considerable pressures.

Nocturnal owls have always been difficult to assess in poorly explored areas. Two in this 'almost unknown' category are the Zaïre Bay-owl, a small dark reddish-brown barn-owl, and the Albertine Owlet, a starling-sized pygmy-owl. Both are known only through odd specimens from montane forest above the western, or Albertine, arm of the Rift Valley. These two evidently have restricted distributions, but they may not be as uncommon as they appear: the Nduk Eagle-owl (37) provides a parallel. The Rufous Fishing-owl, of wetland forest between Sierra Leone and Ghana, is another for which there are fewer than a couple of dozen records.

Some more examples of these 'new' and little-known birds may be added. Schouteden's Swift is represented by five specimens collected since 1956 in a small area of montane forest in eastern Zaïre; fast-flying swifts are often difficult to identify in the field, but this one appears to be confined to an area threatened by deforestation. The White-chested Tinkerbird, a small barbet, is known from just a single individual killed in north-western Zambia in 1964; most barbets are heard more than seen, but even the call of this one remains unrecorded.

Similarly, Prigogine's Ground-thrush is known only from two specimens collected in Kibale Forest, Uganda; and the Red Sea Swallow from a single corpse picked up in 1984, though it is very likely that some as

yet unidentified cliff swallows in southern Ethiopia are the same. The Spot-winged Bulbul of Liberia and the Entebbe Weaver of Uganda are two others only recently described, and the year 1991 saw the naming of both a new boubou shrike from near Bulo Burti in Somalia and Dorst's Cisticola, as well as the discovery of an as yet unpublished new bishop (a weaver).

In most of these cases, and some others later, we have no clear idea of populations or even full ranges, but at least several of the forest species must be threatened. And the Bulo Burti Boubou, thought perhaps to represent a species near extinction because of the almost complete destruction of suitable habitat in that area during civil war, was described from a single bird captured in 1989, studied in captivity, and later released: this was the first new species identified by DNA analysis of feather quills and blood samples.

The fact that there have not yet been any certain extinctions in sub-Saharan Africa and southern Arabia as a whole is more through luck than management. Perhaps it reflects the relative lack of disturbance of birds and their nests by the indigenous peoples over much of tropical Africa (less applicable in Arabia and

North and South Africa), combined with colonial white man's historical concentration on the big mammals for 'sporting' purposes.

Now, with expanding human populations, all sorts of habitat changes and pressures – drainage, widening cultivation, mining, urban development and, especially, deforestation – as well as pollution, pesticides and, not least, the cagebird trade are combining to threaten a greater toll of birdlife. Also, there is a risk of African tourism's beginning to affect, by erosion and disturbance, both the habitats and their wildlife through the very success of what originally appeared to be a conservation asset. Tourism, too, is just one aspect of the greater disturbance now caused in a developing world by increased leisure, whether it be from birders or bathers, walkers or waterskiers, hunters or horsemen. Over 100 of Africa's endemic birds, some 7 per cent of all the resident species, are now giving cause for concern and one-tenth of those have already been classed as 'Endangered'.

One of Africa's few threatened seabirds – indeed, one of the world's rarest terns – is the Damara Tern of the western coast from the Gulf of Guinea to the Cape: its total population is only in the low thousands, and its breeding sites are suffering from development, tourism, and the vegetation growth arising out of dune stabilisation.

The Jackass, Africa's only breeding penguin, is one of four temperate-zone species worldwide to be causing concern (*see* 86): rather similar to the Magellanic and other 'pink-faced' South American penguins, it has declined from a million or two to a hundred thousand or two, originally through excessive commercial collection of eggs and guano – 14 million eggs were taken in the first third of the twentieth century – and latterly through huge declines in fish-stocks resulting from overfishing and oil-spills.

On the subject of seabirds, the Socotra Cormorant is an Arabian endemic brought into prominence by the Gulf War: many were killed by oil, but, although these birds nest only on a few groups of small islands in the

42

WHITE-HEADED ROBIN-CHAT

Cossypha heinrichi

*Robin-chats – small African thrushes 15–22 cm long –
are olive-brown, grey or black above, with rufous
rump and tail-sides, and partly or, more usually, all
rufous below. Some species have plain dark or rufous
heads, others a white stripe over the eyes, or the
central or whole crown white; in this extreme case,
the entire head is white. All are elusive in forest, or
thick undergrowth in woods or gardens, often by
streams, and heard more than seen. Their rich
warbling songs, with mimicry of other birds and
sometimes by night, are among Africa's best. Most of
the 14 species are widespread, even common, but the
White-headed of north Angola and south-west Zaïre
is apparently rare.*

Persian Gulf and possibly around to the Gulf of Aden, they do so in vast colonies of up to tens of thousands and the species is not, as yet, under any threat. Sooty and White-eyed Gulls are also mainly in south Arabia.

Returning to Africa, it is landbirds that are most at risk. Threatened species include quite a few that are endemic to relatively small and isolated areas (or 'islands') of forest, wetland or mountain, particularly the forests and wetlands of single mountains.

Forest birds are much at risk in an age of destruction of trees for all sorts of reasons from hopeless greed to hapless farming. Half-a-dozen regions of lowland or montane forest in Africa give the most cause for concern there because of the number of endemic species they hold. These may be loosely grouped as the rapidly disappearing lowland forests along the West African and Guinea coasts from Sierra Leone to Ghana, and from south-east Nigeria to Gabon; the montane forests of the Cameroon mountains; remnant forest in western Angola; the main block of equatorial forest in Zaïre, particularly in the eastern uplands extending into Uganda, Rwanda and Burundi; upland forests elsewhere in East Africa; the remnant coastal and riverine forest strips of Kenya and Tanzania; and fragmented montane and lowland areas north to Ethiopia and beyond. Let us look at these in turn.

Deep in the Guinea forest, the White-breasted Guineafowl is the smallest and rarest of this essentially African group: a bird of virgin forest that is fast disappearing, it is now confined to a few areas between Sierra Leone and the Ivory Coast; it is classed as 'Endangered', but still hunted. Other specialities of this diminishing strip along the Guinea coast include the little-known Rufous Fishing-owl (p.83); the endangered Western Wattled Cuckoo-shrike (38); and the two picathartes (39). A bulbul with a descriptive name, although the underparts are all yellowish, is the Yellow-throated Olive Greenbul of Senegal to Ghana, often treated as conspecific with two other bulbuls of Senegal to Zaïre: they are not yet threatened, but this bird is, because of the pressures on the Guinea strip.

Honeyguides are remarkable for eating bees' wax and named for the fact that two species noisily lead mammals, including Man, to bees' nests in anticipation that these will then be broken open; 15 species, many of them dull greeny-grey but for white tail-sides, are endemic to Africa. Not described until 1981 and little known, Eisentraut's Honeyguide is evidently rare and at risk from the clearance of the Guinea forests, but it has now been found in four or five widely separated areas from Sierra Leone to Cameroon.

One of this honeyguide's localities is Mount Nimba, a general area that it shares with the Liberian Black Flycatcher that is similarly known from only five forest zones, one already largely felled, between Guinea and the Ivory Coast. Other threatened Gulf of Guinea birds with restricted ranges are two forest weavers. The black and yellow Gola Malimbe, first described in 1974, is limited to an area between Sierra Leone and the Ivory Coast; Bates's Weaver – green and yellow, with head chestnut and black (male) or all-black (female) – is rare in lowland forest in south Cameroon.

Although not forest birds, another weaver and a waxbill may be mentioned here. The black and red Ibadan Malimbe is found in open country with palms

43
AFRICAN PEAFOWL
Afropavo congensis

All but one of nearly 50 pheasants are Asiatic (64). This exception, in the upper Zaïre forests, has the character of other peafowl (67) but is two-thirds the size with only a rudimentary train of slightly elongated tail-coverts. The bronze-green male has a black head with bare bluish face and red neck-sides, a narrow black crest and adjacent tuft of white bristles, and touches of blue on chest, back, shoulders and 'tail'. Throat inflated, he bows, raises and fans his tail, and turns drooped wings forward, like other peafowl. The paler green female has crest, head and underbody rufous. Shy, terrestrial, omnivorous, this bird is hunted but threatened more by deforestation.

44
NAHAN'S FRANCOLIN
Francolinus nahani

The francolins are a genus of more than 40 small to medium-sized partridges, mostly African, the rest southern Asiatic. Some are widely distributed or locally numerous, others restricted in range, and a few rare. The last are mainly forest species confined to single highland regions. Only 20–25 cm long, Nahan's is a shy and elusive bird of dense forest at 1000–1500 m in north-east Zaïre and west Uganda. Like the commoner Forest Francolin, it is black below edged with white, but recognised by black marks on the brown back, by its whiter throat, and by red eye-patches and legs. All francolins are much hunted; but this one is also losing its forests and at risk because of its small range.

and other trees, but has such a tiny range that it is already classed as 'Endangered' by the spread of intensive agriculture, even though it has sometimes been seen on farmland. The Anambra Waxbill – brownish with scarlet rump and red bill – is endemic to south-east Nigeria and has always been very local in long-grass areas in open forest or by rivers.

The forests of Mount Cameroon and of the highland complexes running some 600 km north-east from it along the Cameroon–Nigeria border are the homes of several vulnerable species. The rare Cameroon Mountain Francolin is a good example of a threatened forest 'island' bird. Other specialities of the highlands to the north-east include Bannerman's Turaco (**40**); the Green-breasted Bush-shrike (**41**); and the greyer Serle's Bush-shrike, endemic to Mount Kupé, which has a black mask and a white throat.

Also in Cameroon are the tiny highland ranges of the Banded Wattle-eye – a blue-black and white flycatcher, with black chest-band and red eye-wattles, now classed as 'Endangered' – and the mainly rufous White-throated Mountain Babbler. Bannerman's Weaver is another scarce mountain-forest bird of the Nigeria–Cameroon border. Several more species of Mount Cameroon and the adjacent highlands, such as the Cameroon Mountain Robin-chat, also have very restricted ranges, but are locally not uncommon.

An isolated forest strip extends northwards from around Gabela in western Angola, some of it already secondary growth combined with coffee. Endemic and little-known specialities here include the Angola Helmet-shrike and Monteiro's Bush-shrike (both representatives of essentially African groups), the Gabela Akalat (a bush-robin), and Pulitzer's Longbill (a warbler). The mountains of south-west Angola also hold a partridge of restricted range, Swierstra's Francolin, and the Angola–Zaïre borders the rare White-headed Robin-chat (**42**).

But it is not just the narrower western strips of forest that are under threat. Forest species throughout Africa are at risk, even if in the less disturbed reaches of Zaïre

this is in the longer term. The African Peafowl (**43**) is an example of a large bird that evidently has a fairly wide range but needs extensive and secluded forest; if most of the forest disappears, so will it. Other important African forest species in the same category are the Zaïre Serpent-eagle and the Long-tailed Hawk.

A particularly rich area of mainly lowland forest is that of eastern Zaïre, with outliers in west and south Uganda. Specialities here include Nahan's Francolin (**44**), while two rare forest weavers – the Yellow-legged and the Golden-naped – were 'lost' for several decades until rediscovered in mid 1980s. Oberländer's Ground-thrush is another lowland rarity of eastern-most Zaïre and western Uganda, while the related Prigogine's Ground-thrush (*p.83*) is probably a bird of medium elevations; altitudinal limits are significant for a number of upland birds.

45
ROCKEFELLER'S SUNBIRD
Nectarinia rockefelleri

The sunbirds – some 120 species – are mainly African but extend to the Malagasy region, southern Asia, and Australia. Some are tiny, only 8 cm long, others twice as large; a few are almost doubled again by long central tail-feathers. All have thin curved bills: the shorter-billed feed more on insects, and the longer-billed more on nectar. Males are often colourful and iridescent, females duller. Rockefeller's is rare and confined to moorland and streamside thickets at 3000 m in east Zaïre. The male, with a graduated violet-black tail, is one of several montane sunbirds with shiny green heads and red and yellow or white underparts; he is whitish below with red breast-band and tail-coverts.

WHITE-WINGED APALIS

Apalis chariessa

*The apalises are a genus of about 20 shy African forest warblers, related to other
Old World warblers but mostly with longish and highly mobile tails. Some are
colourful; this one is among the most striking. Glossy blue-black and brown
above with white wing-patches and lateral tail-tips, the male has a black strip
separating white throat from orange chest and yellow belly; the green-backed
female is otherwise greyer where the male is black. Formerly in forest areas and
riverside strips from Kenya to Mozambique, it is now evidently one of the rarest
apalises and also threatened by deforestation. One or two others have adapted to
scrub and cultivation; it seems less likely that this species can.*

Thus, the borders of Zaïre with Uganda and Tanzania, including Rwanda and Burundi – straddled by a region of mountain forests – include a number of endemic birds threatened by tiny ranges and restricted habitats. The almost unknown Zaïre Bay-owl and Albertine Owlet have already been mentioned, along with Schouteden's Swift. The African Green Broadbill is confined to three areas of mountain forest around 2000 m on the Zaïre–Uganda border: this is the rarest of a tropical family of 14 dumpy and colourful birds of Africa to south-east Asia and the Philippines.

Prigogine's Greenbul is a yellow-green bulbul with a whitish face: originally discovered among birds collected near Lake Edward, it was subsequently also located west of Lake Albert on the next mountain 'island' to the north-east. Like this bulbul, the Marungu Sunbird – a race of the Greater Double-collared, or perhaps a distinct species – nests at lower altitudes than Rockefeller's (**45**).

A flycatcher and two warblers of this part of Africa are more medium-elevation forest birds, above 1500 m. The rare Chapin's Flycatcher is known only from the Zaïre–Uganda borders and the Kakamega Forest area in western Kenya. Turner's Eremomela is another now confined to easternmost Zaïre and Kakamega; while Prigogine's Apalis is endemic to the middle heights of Mount Kabobo in eastern Zaïre.

Other threatened forest warblers, together with a couple of small thrushes and a starling, are either endemic to Kenya or Tanzania, or have wider but very patchy ranges down to Mozambique or even South Africa. These include the rare White-winged Apalis (**46**); and the grey and white Kungwe Apalis, endemic to riverine and upland forest between 1200 and 2200 m in western Tanzania. Swynnerton's Bush-robin, with black and white gorgets separating grey head and rich buff breast, is still locally not uncommon in higher mountain forests around the Zimbabwe–Mozambique border; but the Cholo Alethe, whose most striking features are white throat and tail-corners, is classed as 'Endangered' at its slightly lower levels on the Malawi–Mozambique border. Abbott's Starling is another highland-forest bird of Kenya and Tanzania that is already uncommon except in two small areas.

Sokoke, an important lowland coastal forest in Kenya, has several threatened birds: the Sokoke Scops-owl (**47**) and Clarke's Weaver are endemic, and it is the stronghold of the Sokoke Pipit (**48**). The East Coast Akalat also has its stronghold in Sokoke, but extends to a few other forest patches south to Mozambique. The Taita Olive Thrush is confined to the Taita and Kasigau Hills of south-east Kenya, and the boldly marked Spotted Ground-thrush, although locally distributed through six countries from southern Sudan to South Africa, is everywhere rare and threatened by forest destruction.

Birds of isolated forested uplands in eastern Tanzania, especially the Usambaras and Ulugurus, include the Nduk Eagle-owl (**37**) and the strikingly chestnut-headed Mrs Moreau's Warbler, which is endemic to forest undergrowth at around 2000 m. The short-tailed Amani Sunbird is found in Sokoke and the lower Usambaras, and the Banded Green Sunbird is endemic to higher parts of the Usambaras and possibly the Ngurus and Ulugurus farther south; both are locally common in primary and secondary forest but at risk because of very restricted ranges.

Other birds endemic to these mountain 'islands' of east Tanzania include the dull-looking Usambara Ground-robin and, farther south, the rather similar Iringa Ground-robin; the chestnut-tailed Dappled Mountain Robin, of the well separated Usambaras and Uzungwe Mountains of Tanzania and Namuli Mountains of Mozambique; the Usambara Weaver, which is a black and yellow forest weaver with green-brown head and rufous chest-patch; the blue-black, dark green and yellow Uluguru Bush-shrike, which apparently has an exceptionally small range; and the Rufous-winged Sunbird, not even discovered until 1981. The Long-billed Apalis, once essentially a forest bird of the Usambaras, and of one small area in Mozambique, is now local and uncommon in vines in

cultivated valleys in the hills. Other such adaptations may be necessary by other small forest birds if they are to survive.

Moving farther north, the critically endangered Dorst's Francolin is confined to two small, decreasing and ever more disturbed areas of forest in Djibouti. Ruspoli's Turaco (*see under* **40**) lives only in a few small areas of threatened juniper forest and acacia woodland in southern Ethiopia.

If threats to forest affect the greatest number of Africa's rare, vulnerable or endangered birds, it must not be forgotten that wetlands are also at risk. The Shoebill, the sole species in one of Africa's endemic families, is confined to overgrown swamps in south Sudan, south-west Ethiopia, Uganda, locally in west Tanzania, and in south-east Zaïre and north-west Zambia. This is quite a large range but, even if, as now seems likely, the published population figure of not more than 1500 is a gross underestimate and the former widespread taking of young for zoos no longer applies, the species needs extensive swamps and is threatened by drainage and water diversion, agricultural development, and increased cattle grazing.

47
SOKOKE SCOPS-OWL
Otus ireneae

A third of the 175 owls are scops-owls, missing only from north Eurasia and much of Australasia. Most call repeatedly and are small with more or less obvious 'ear-tufts'. In Africa, two are widespread; five more have tiny ranges. The smallest of these, only 16 cm long, is endemic to Sokoke Forest in lowland coastal Kenya. Like many owls, it has yellow eyes and two colour morphs, one a mix of grey-brown and dark brown, the other rufous. Numbers have been put at 1300–2000 pairs, but a big part of Sokoke has been felled and this owl needs a certain tree size on red sand; it is absent if the canopy is below 4 m or the sand is white. An ICBP conservation programme began in 1989.

Two other birds with populations now reduced to the lower end of the four-figure range are the Slaty Egret (**49**) and Southern Bald Ibis. The latter, like its relative in the south Palearctic (*see* **28**), has declined, but probably more from disturbance of its colonies, the taking of young, and loss of feeding habitat resulting in higher chick mortality, than from pesticides.

The white-necked and grey-bodied Wattled Crane has a much larger, but very patchy, range in marshy wetlands from South Africa to Ethiopia: killed for food in the south and, like all cranes (*see* **29**), needing undisturbed marshland for breeding, its decreasing population of only a few thousands makes it of special concern. Another wetland bird known in Ethiopia and South Africa, but hardly anywhere in between, is the White-winged Pygmy Crake, threatened by drought in the north and drainage elsewhere.

Wetland drainage also affects a number of small birds. For example, Grauer's Rush-warbler is limited to certain threatened highland swamps on the Zaïre–Uganda–Rwanda–Burundi borders. The Giant or Dja River Rush-warbler of the Cameroon–Gabon borders is vulnerable because of its small numbers and limited range. The Papyrus Yellow Warbler has a wider range, from western Kenya–Uganda to eastern Zaïre–Zambia, but is generally rare and, because it is confined to the one habitat, also at risk from papyrus-cutting.

Other birds are scarce in very limited ranges, which makes them that much more vulnerable to habitat changes and local threats. Botha's Lark and the aptly named Yellow-breasted Pipit are confined to small areas of high veld and other mountain grassland, mainly in southern Transvaal and the Orange Free State. The Loango Slender-billed Weaver is restricted to the coast from Gabon to the mouth of the Zaïre River, and there are at least two other little-known and very local weavers in Zaïre (one of them also in Angola), as well as the Black-faced Waxbill of lowland grass around Lake Upemba.

Similarly, Hinde's Pied Babbler is extremely local and uncommon in valleys and semi-arid bushland south of Mount Kenya. And the Tana River Cisticola, one of Africa's myriad of sometimes almost indistinguishable grass-warblers, is another little-known endemic with a very restricted range in semi-arid bushland in east Kenya.

Farther north, the Somali Pigeon is a rock dove of the cliffs and dry mountain crags of the horn of Africa, where the upland junipers of the extreme north-east also hold the rare Somali or Warsangli Linnet. The White-tailed Swallow is endemic to a small area of southern Ethiopia at around the 2000-m mark. The Ankober Serin apparently inhabits only cliff country 100 km to the north-east of Adis Abeba; and the Yellow-throated Serin, another small finch of the same highland Ethiopian province, long known only from three specimens collected in the 1880s, was suddenly found again in 1989. Stresemann's Bush-crow – grey and white with blue-black wings and tail, and bare blue skin around the eyes – is confined to thornbush in southern Ethiopia and, rather surprisingly because it is such a distinctive bird, was not discovered until 1938.

It is not nearly so remarkable that this last corner of Africa has produced three new larks in the past decade or two. Most larks are not particularly striking to look at, and two-thirds of the world's species live in the Afrotropical region: some are little-known, and it is not always clear how local or how much at risk they are. The 'new' trio are Ash's Lark, of southern coastal Somalia, and the Degodi Lark and Sidamo Long-clawed Lark, both of southern Ethiopia; the first at least is locally common. Two other long-clawed larks, the Somali and the South African, are often treated as widely separated races of one species: the former's range is very restricted and the latter's contracting, so that both may be at risk from spreading cultivation.

At least a quarter of Africa's raptors are decreasing through deforestation, felling of tall old nesting trees, drainage, spread of cultivation, pesticides and so on (though, conversely, these changes are helping such others as the Black-shouldered Kite and Long-crested Eagle, as well as the urbanised Black Kite). Decreasing are forest accipiters, some snake-eagles and true eagles, the African Marsh Harrier and Palmnut Vulture, and several typical vultures, but few as yet to the point of being seriously threatened.

The Cape Vulture of South Africa is, however, causing concern. It continues to decline through poisoning and shooting, accidental electrocution at pylons, shortages of carrion in an age when ranching practices quickly dispose of dead animals, and a significant proportion of rickets among chicks deprived of the calcium normally derived from bone fragments. Now this large vulture has a population of under 10,000 and, in the long term, seems threatened with extinction.

Several raptors, such as the Bateleur, and a variety of other birds, large and small, have relatively recently been found to be resident not only in sub-Saharan parts of the region, but in south-west Arabia too. This area, particularly Yemen, also holds eleven endemic land-birds: of these, the Socotra Cisticola, found only on the Yemeni island whose name it bears, and the Yemen Thrush, only in the mountains of south-west Arabia, are rare even within their restricted ranges.

Several more birds of south-west Arabia, mainly seed-eaters, are otherwise found only in adjacent Somalia or Ethiopia. But most of the Arabian birds mentioned in these two paragraphs live on thinly vegetated and rather inaccessible slopes of hills and mountains between 1500 m and 3000 m or more. Thus, although many of their ranges are small, none is threatened by Man's activities.

The cagebird trade is as big a problem in parts of the Afrotropical region, particularly West Africa, as it is elsewhere in the world. But, in contrast to South America (*chapter 2*), for example, relatively few species are as yet seriously threatened by it: this is, of course, partly because there are only 19 parrots in Africa compared with, say, more than 50 in Australia and well over 100 in South America. Nevertheless, one small parrot already affected is the Black-cheeked Lovebird; it has a restricted range in wooded river valleys in southern Zambia and is still illegally trapped.

SOKOKE PIPIT

Anthus sokokensis

*Unlike the Sokoke Scops-owl (**47**), this bird is not confined to Sokoke. But
it is otherwise found only in two or three much smaller areas of relict
evergreen forest in coastal Kenya and Tanzania; moreover, it has become
rare in Tanzania through mining and deforestation. Sokoke is the
stronghold, but even there extensive felling in the 1980s apparently caused
a decrease. Most pipits are unspectacular, except in song-flight, and this
one is no exception, being warm buff above and cream below, with black
streaking, but it is of special interest. Many of the world's 38 pipits live in
more or less open country, but the Sokoke inhabits glades and other less
closed parts of forest areas.*

SLATY EGRET
Egretta vinaceigula

*Many egrets are white (26), but this one is pale slate-grey with a vinous-red to buff throat
and foreneck and, sometimes, varying mixes of vinous-red in the chest-plumes and on the
blacker belly and flanks; the legs stand out as yellow to yellow-green. It is shaped more like
a small Little Egret than the dumpy Black Egret with which it might be confused. An
uncommon bird in parts of Zambia, Botswana, Namibia and perhaps Angola, chiefly
where those countries meet, it favours floodplains with receding water levels. It feeds
mainly on fish, frequently foraging in shallows hidden by vegetation. Apparently
decreasing, it is at risk where its specialised feeding areas are drained or dammed.*

Sub-Saharan Africa has two main groups of associated inshore islands. The first – Pemba, Zanzibar and Mafia, off the coast of Tanzania – has few endemic birds, though the Pemba Scops-owl, sometimes treated as a race of the Madagascar Scops-owl but surely specifically distinct, may not be as common as it once was. The status of the Pemba Green Pigeon is not clear.

On the other hand, the series of islands that extends south-west from Cameroon into the Gulf of Guinea – Bioko, Príncipe, São Tomé, and Annobon – holds a remarkable collection of endemic birds. Most are on São Tomé and Príncipe, even though these two islands are only around 250 km from the African coast. Some, such as the São Tomé Green and Bronze-naped Pigeons (the latter also on Príncipe and Annobon), are common enough to be considered not at risk, despite their restricted ranges. Others are at much lower densities. The Dwarf Olive Ibis, Newton's Fiscal Shrike (**36**) and the all-brown São Tomé Grosbeak, having not been seen for over 50 years until their rediscovery in 1988–91, were long feared extinct (*p.83*). Several more are classed as 'Vulnerable' or 'Rare'.

Among the scarcer birds of these islands are the São Tomé Maroon Pigeon; the São Tomé Scops-owl; the São Tomé Short-tail (a forest warbler); the Príncipe White-eye (of São Tomé too) and the Bioko and Príncipe Speirops (large white-eyes); the Príncipe Drongo; and, not least, the São Tomé Giant Sunbird and Giant Weaver, each the largest of its kind. Just as the São Tomé Grosbeak is a very big finch, so these last two are further examples of the gigantism that is sometimes a feature of long-isolated island species.

Finally, seven of the endemic species on the four South Atlantic island groups are classed as 'Rare'. Taking the northernmost group first, Ascension Island – or, rather, Boatswainbird Island off its north-east shore – holds the entire breeding population of the Ascension Frigatebird, which is not so much more numerous than the Christmas Frigatebird (*see* **76**); the population appears to have declined over the past 30 years and is highly vulnerable to disturbance.

On St Helena, some 1300 km to the south-east, the St Helena Plover totals only a few hundreds. These live entirely on grassland and plough, never on the shore; threats include changing habitat and predation of eggs and young by introduced cats, rats and Common Mynahs (the last very numerous and possibly even competing with the plovers for food).

Whereas Ascension and St Helena are single islands with just one or two islets close inshore, the somewhat smaller Tristan da Cunha, 2500 km farther south, has several associated islands about 30 km away, the largest of which, Inaccessible, holds the flightless Inaccessible Rail; this still has a reasonable population, but in the last three centuries the world's islands have lost more than a dozen rails, many of them flightless, for a variety of reasons but particularly through Man's introduction of mammal predators (*chapters 5 and 8*). The long extinct Ascension Rail, likewise flightless, was closely related to the one on Inaccessible; and, as already noted, there used also to be a Tristan Moorhen until about a hundred years ago.

Two related buntings of these islands are the only two in an endemic genus that is probably of South American origin: the Tristan Bunting, extinct on Tristan itself, survives quite successfully on the other main islands of the group, but only a hundred or two Grosbeak Buntings remain on the islands of Inaccessible and Nightingale.

Gough Island, a further 400 km away to the southeast, also has its own Gough Bunting (again in the low hundreds) and Gough Moorhen (more numerous). Both would be seriously threatened if cats and rats were to become established.

Madagascar and western Indian Ocean islands

Because Australia is ranked as a continent, Madagascar – or the Malagasy Republic – is the world's fourth largest island after Greenland, New Guinea and Borneo. It is geologically old and, although a mere 400 km off the south-east coast of Africa, has probably been separated for over 50 million years.

Although it is often considered part of the Afrotropical region, its mammals, birds and other animals are, despite its proximity to Africa, so different that it is now usually regarded as a distinct (sub)region that otherwise takes in various small islands of the western Indian Ocean. The affinities of the bats, birds, reptiles and plants of those other archipelagos are mainly with Madagascar, but also show links with south-east Asia. Certain Malagasy and Asiatic genera of owls, bulbuls and thrushes, for example, are not found anywhere in Africa at all.

Even Madagascar's peoples are not African: they too originate from south-east Asia 5000 km away to the north-east. Madagascar was first settled in about 500 BC from the Indonesian islands, and then again during AD 800–1200. From the eighth century onwards, its coasts were increasingly visited by Arab and African traders. But it is only four or five hundred years since Europeans began discovering this and the various much smaller islands in the western Indian Ocean. The result has been an ecological disaster.

Slaughter by hungry sailors contributed to the extinction of some remarkable flightless birds, though the animals the ships brought with them probably played as big a part in the destruction. The wildlife of islands is particularly vulnerable to introductions of rats, cats and other predators, and also of robust birds that are similar enough to endemic species in food requirements and behaviour to compete with them.

No less serious, and still continuing, has been the destruction of as great a proportion of natural forest as anywhere in the world. Some has been replaced by secondary growth, but in the process various forest species have been lost and others are in great danger. Much of Madagascar itself was once covered by dense evergreen and deciduous forest, but most has been cleared: fifty years ago over 30,000 square km were still forested; now less than one-tenth of that remains.

Zoologically, Madagascar is probably best known for its endemic mammals: most notable among these are the lemurs and the tenrecs. Until Man arrived to hunt, to cut and burn trees, and to introduce domestic animals, there were at least 40 species of the primitive primates known as lemurs; more than 20 still survive, of which the largest are monkey-sized and the smallest no bigger than a mouse. The 30-odd tenrecs are hardly less diversified, variously looking somewhat like hedgehogs, moles, shrews or even otters. Madagascar also has half the world's chameleons.

Some 1600 km long and mostly about a quarter as wide, Madagascar has three main longitudinal zones. The roughly quadrilateral central granitic plateau at 800 m to 1500 m, with scattered volcanic peaks up to 2500 m or more, has been largely deforested for timber exports, building materials and fuel, and developed for living, ricefields, and subsistence farming: it suffers from serious erosion. On the steeper east side is a narrow coastal strip, with most of the island's remaining forest on the escarpment, and to the more sloping west a wide band of broken hills and plains.

The eastern side is wet, with a rainfall of up to 350 cm in the northern section; the west is much drier, with less than one-fifth of the rain, and varies from patches of wooded savannah to thin scrub and prairie grassland. The south-west and extreme south have a subdesert climate with thorns, cactuses and dwarf baobabs. Rivers flow mostly to the west; the east has many small torrents and waterfalls. Alaotra, 40 km long, is the largest of a number of volcanic lakes.

This huge island provides 99 per cent of the landmass that, at only just over 600,000 square km, makes this far smaller than any of the six continental regions – though, of course, the tropical Pacific islands (*chapter 8*) total less than one-twelfth of that size.

The small archipelagos that, with Madagascar, make up the Malagasy region are, to the north-west, the Comoros and the Aldabra group; to the north, various islands up to the granitic Seychelles; and, to the east, the volcanic Mascarenes, where Man's destruction has been most thorough. It is also convenient to include here the Prince Edward, Crozet, St Paul and Amsterdam Islands some 2000 km south of Madagascar and the Mascarenes, leaving Kerguelen and Heard Island to the Antarctic region (*chapter 9*).

The four volcanic islands of the Comoros total only 2200 square km. The largest, Gran Comoro, rises to 2600 m and even the smallest, Mohéli, to nearly 600 m. The Aldabra archipelago also consists of four islands, but these are raised coral limestone atolls; they are administratively part of Seychelles 800 km away to the north-east, but lie much closer to Madagascar.

Apart from two sand-cays on coral reefs to the north, the main Seychelles include some 30 small granitic islands and islets. Between them and the Aldabra archipelago, and also administratively part of Seychelles, are the low-lying coral limestones of the Amirantes, Providence, St Pierre and the Farquhars. The total area of Seychelles is a mere 400 square km, but the granitic islands are the peaks of a vast submarine plateau, with extensive coral banks, extending down towards Mauritius.

50
CROSSLEY'S GROUND-ROLLER
Atelornis crossleyi

The five ground-rollers are endemic to Madagascar; of four now rare, three are confined to remnant eastern rainforest. Unlike the typical rollers of Eurasia and Africa – and the Cuckoo-roller, also found only in Madagascar and the Comoros – ground-rollers are terrestrial and unobtrusive. Despite its mainly rufous head and underbody, streaked collar, and green back, rump and tail, Crossley's – plump and some 25 cm long – is easily missed in the shadows of low tangles or fallen branches below a dense canopy. It tends to fly only to escape danger; hunting insects, it normally runs, then stands motionless. Nesting ground-rollers dig tunnels half a metre long and ending in a chamber.

As the world's only mid-ocean granitic outcrops, the inner Seychelles may have been cut off from other landmasses longer than any islands that are not either volcanic or coral. The central mountain ridge of Mahé rises abruptly from near the coast with steep-sided ravines to a maximum of over 900 m. Much of the original forest of endemic palms, screwpines and other

51
MADAGASCAR SERPENT-EAGLE
Eutriorchis astur

Long thought extinct, with no sure record for nearly 60 years, this rare Madagascan endemic was seen in 1988 and a corpse found elsewhere in 1990. It needs undisturbed rainforest: though large tracts remain intact in the east, continuing clearance threatens. Some 65 cm long, grey-brown and obscurely banded above, with thin white barring on shoulders and neck-sides, and white below with close dark bars, this raptor has short broad wings spanning little over a metre, and a long rounded tail. Pattern and shape recall a big Henst's Goshawk, another Madagascan forest endemic. The latter eats birds; the serpent-eagle probably specialises on the many chameleons of this large island.

trees has been cleared, originally for maize and now for coconut, vanilla, cinnamon and tea. Except for the remarkable stands of coco-de-mer palms preserved on Praslin, only isolated individuals and patches of the primary tree cover remain.

Turning to the Mascarenes, the three volcanic basalt islands of Mauritius, Réunion and Rodrigues extend in a line east of Madagascar, separated from it and each other by several hundred kilometres of deep water. All are hilly to mountainous with rocky spurs and deep ravines, and many small streams. Originally the cover was wooded savannah and dry evergreen forest, now replaced by scrub and introduced trees.

Mauritius is probably the best known. It is also central in position and size, with an area of over 1800 square km and a maximum height of over 800 m; half-a-dozen islets – like the smaller islands of Seychelles, holding large seabird colonies – extend in a string north-east from the northernmost point. Réunion, 200 km to the south-west, is the largest of the Mascarenes, at just over 2500 square km, and much the highest with one peak over 3000 m. Rodrigues lies more than 500 km east of Mauritius and is far smaller, barely more than 100 square km and rising to less than 400 m, but probably older; it too has more than a dozen offshore islets of basalt, coral and sand.

The four southerly archipelagos of the Prince Edward, Crozet, St Paul and Amsterdam Islands are also volcanic, with peaks between 500 and 1200 m, but are mostly smaller than Rodrigues and either rather bare or with a dense cover of mosses and lichens.

Apart from these, the Malagasy region proper lies largely between the equator and the Tropic of Capricorn. Thus, the climate is mainly tropical though influenced by altitude and interactions of the south-east trade and north-west monsoon winds. It tends to be warmer and wetter during the monsoon in November–April and cooler and drier under the influence of the trade winds in the rest of the year.

Cyclones are not uncommon and often destructive during December–March, especially in the south;

damage can be a significant factor where forests have already been depleted. The near-equatorial Seychelles, however, lie outside the cyclone belt. Temperatures in Madagascar are 10–26°C in July and 16–29°C in December. The Seychelles are more constant, in the range 24–30°C at sea-level, with a high humidity. With similar temperatures, the more subtropical Mascarenes are hot in November–April, cooler in May–October; Réunion's peak is, as its name of Piton des Neiges suggests, high enough to have frequent snow.

Indigenous birds

Madagascar's most distinctive indigenous birds include 27 species in five families that occur nowhere else, except that two of these families are also represented in the Comoros.

52

MADAGASCAR GREBE
Tachybaptus pelzelnii

Madagascar has three of the four small grebes known as dabchicks: this and the Alaotra Grebe are endemic. Both have decreased since the 1930s when Little Grebes arrived and spread as introduced herbivorous fish cleared aquatic vegetation. Many habitats are now too open for the first two, which compete for food and even hybridise with the third. Other problems are hunting, rice-growing, fish-farming and pollution. The Madagascar is stockier than the Little, with a longer pale bill, no gape-patches, a white line below a black cap, rufous-flecked neck, and longer wings. Under 50 Alaotra Grebes may remain: tiny with longer dark bills, pale eyes, no rufous, dusky underbody, and short wings.

First, the three mesites are curious terrestrial birds that run like pigeons, bob like gallinules, and rarely fly, and even then only for short distances. In some ways they resemble rails, to which they are distantly related, and in others they behave more like babblers, with which they are certainly not connected. The Brown Mesite is rufous and grey, with whitish markings above and below the eyes. The White-breasted Mesite has a whitish-streaked head, and a whitish chest spotted with black. The third species, Bensch's Monia, is greyish above with white supercilia; the throat and chest of the male are whitish with black spots, and of the female mottled chestnut. The three respectively inhabit forest, woodland and subdesert scrub.

The next two endemic families – the five ground-rollers and the single Cuckoo-roller, or Courol – probably represent separate invasions by ancestral stocks of rollers, a colourful family widely distributed in, especially, Africa and Asia. These Madagascan birds have become sufficiently distinct to be regarded as separate families. The relatively dull-coloured ground-rollers have large heads and stout bills not unlike the true rollers, but short wings and, being

53
MADAGASCAR RED OWL
Tyto soumagnei

Only two-thirds as big as its relative, the widespread Barn-owl, and much darker, this frog-eating rarity of the humid rainforests of eastern Madagascar likewise has a clear facial disc, but the white is tinged orange and the whole outlined in deeper orange; head and body are all red-orange speckled with black. A number were shot by collectors in the late 1800s and early 1900s, but only one has been seen in the past 50 years. The nest is unknown. Even so, the species is very likely still to be in existence somewhere, as its habitat is forested mountains where it would be strictly nocturnal and have an unfamiliar range of calls. 'Wok wok wok' and a brief alarm are the only sounds on record.

primarily terrestrial, longer legs; Crossley's Ground-roller (50) and three of the others are forest birds, while the Long-tailed Ground-roller's range is confined to subdesert scrub.

The Cuckoo-roller is arboreal, noisy and more conspicuous, often circling over forest or woodland; its call is a striking series of three 'kwi-yu' notes, decreasing in volume and ending with a short 'kwi'. Unlike all other rollers, the sexes look very different: males are iridescent slate above and grey below; females are dark brown and variably rufous, spotted with black below.

The fourth endemic family includes a variety of primitive forest songbirds known as asities and sunbird-asities. The two asities are stout, short-tailed, broad-billed and solitary fruit-eaters about 15 cm in length, and black or olive with varying yellow. The two insectivorous sunbird-asities, although unrelated to the Afro-Asian sunbirds and less flitting and active, have converged to resemble them in size, in their curved bills for flower-probing, and in the general appearance of their breeding and non-breeding plumages.

The vangas are the last and largest of these five endemic families. Variously 12–30 cm long and boldly pied, blue and white, or black, rufous and grey, the 14 species are mostly noisy, gregarious and insectivorous.

But the total of endemic birds in Madagascar and the Comoros is far greater than the 27 in these distinct families. Of the 197 species that breed there, 180 are landbirds; of these 180, almost three-fifths are confined to Madagascar and the total is brought up to nearly three-quarters when a further 25 shared only with the Comoros are included. No less than 94 per cent of the passerines, or perching birds, are endemic. Even so, compared with all the continental regions, the total number of species is small; any single sub-Saharan African area of varied habitats and similar size would probably have at least 500–600 breeding species.

On the debit side, Madagascar lacks many African families and other groups, such as ostriches – which were once replaced by the now extinct elephantbirds (*p.106*) – secretarybirds, guineafowls, cranes, turacos, wood-hoopoes, hornbills, mousebirds, barbets, wood-peckers, honeyguides, broadbills, pittas, helmet-shrikes and, notably, oxpeckers, finches, buffalo-weavers and widowbirds. (Broadbills are perhaps replaced by the asities; and helmet-shrikes by the vangas, two of which also fill the wood-hoopoe and nuthatch niches.) Three of Africa's numerous families – larks, starlings and waxbills – each have but a single species here, and there are only four weavers. Fruit-eaters and seed-eaters are poorly represented.

Some 30 species of landbirds are found on each of the four islands of the Comoros and, apart from the 25 that are shared only with Madagascar, eight are endemic to that group.

The Aldabra archipelago holds ten species of land-birds that are found only there and on Madagascar or the Comoros, but does not share any with the rest of Seychelles apart from the widespread Malagasy Turtle-dove. None of these is threatened, although introduced cats and rats prey on any small birds, while goats damage the vegetation. But Aldabra also holds two endemic species of its own. The first is the Aldabra Drongo, one of four drongos in the Malagasy region: two in the Comoros are threatened species (*p.112*), but this one is widespread in dense scrub, casuarina woodland and mangroves. The other endemic is the Aldabra Brush-warbler, critically endangered if not already extinct (*p.113*).

The three islands of the Mascarenes together have some 15 endemic species, well under half of the total before Man arrived. Apart from the 11 discussed in the section on 'Threatened birds', these include another petrel (Réunion), a bulbul (with distinct races on Réunion and Mauritius), and a paradise-flycatcher and a white-eye (the last two on both those islands). There is also a distinctive swiftlet, now usually treated as conspecific with a widespread species of south-east Asia, as well as a well-marked race of the Stonechat that is very common on Réunion.

Seabirds, especially shearwaters, tropicbirds, frigatebirds, boobies and terns, are well represented in the region, mainly on less inhabited islets. Some of the southerly island groups, particularly Amsterdam, have large concentrations of less tropical families: penguins, albatrosses, petrels, cormorants, skuas and gulls.

Introductions

Surprisingly in view of what has happened on islands elsewhere, particularly New Zealand (*chapter 7*) and the Hawaiian group (*chapter 8*), introduced birds are not a problem on Madagascar

54
AMSTERDAM ALBATROSS
Diomedea amsterdamensis

Albatrosses live mainly in southern oceans – although one is tropical, in the Galápagos, and three more are north Pacific. Two confined to single island groups are classed as 'Endangered': this one, discovered only in the late 1970s, has under ten pairs on Amsterdam Island in the southern Indian Ocean and a total population, including immatures, of less than 50. Among the largest of all the 14 albatrosses, spanning 3 m or more, it is dark with a white face, belly and underwings, thus resembling the dark immature Wandering Albatross. It is identified by the dark tips and cutting edges to its mandibles and, in flight, also by its dusky thigh-patches and inner leading edges to the underwings.

itself. Indeed, only two are widely naturalised: Feral Rock Pigeons, brought in by the early European settlers, and Common Mynahs, introduced in the late nineteenth century and now well distributed along the east coast and in parts of the south and north-west.

House Sparrows have long been established in the Comoros, but did not arrive in Madagascar until about 1984, perhaps by ship, and are still found only in the region of the eastern port of Toamasina. Common Waxbills were recorded in another area in 1983, but evidently died out, and rumours of introduced Helmeted Guineafowls have never been proved.

On the other hand, although not on the scale found in the Pacific, a number of birds have been introduced to Seychelles and the Mascarenes. Indeed, in inner Seychelles the three commonest landbirds are the naturalised Barred Ground-doves, Common Mynahs and Madagascar Fodies; all three are in such numbers as to be competing for food and habitat with indigenous species. Common Mynahs are considered to be a factor in the poor success of the tiny remnant population of Seychelles Magpie-robins (*p.113*). In the Mascarenes, similarly, introduced Ring-necked Parakeets and Madagascar Fodies are serious competitors of related endemics.

But in Seychelles the worst problems have been caused by the Department of Agriculture's decision in the early 1950s to introduce Common Barn-owls, with the untested aim of controlling rats. They had no effect on the rats, but concentrated instead on birds, particularly White or Fairy Terns which they soon almost wiped out on the largest islands.

Similarly, although not intentionally introduced, some House Crows – an Indian and south-eastern Asiatic species – arrived on board a ship in 1978 and became established; had they been allowed to increase without control, they might well have become as big a threat to the local small landbirds as their naturalised populations are on the African coast (*chapter 4*).

Other introduced birds of these islands include Grey Francolins on Desroches, House Sparrows in the

55
SEYCHELLES GREY WHITE-EYE
Zosterops modesta

The white-eyes are an African, south Asiatic and Australasian family, so named for their variably conspicuous 'spectacles' of tiny white feathers. Fussy little warbler-like birds, gregarious and vocal, they live on insects, nectar and fruit. Many of some 90 species, all but about ten of them island forms, are greenish and yellow. But, of the half-dozen in the Malagasy region, two are mainly brown-grey. Once numerous in mountain forest on Mahé, though not known on any other island, Seychelles Grey White-eyes are now reduced to 50–100. Probably deforestation has played a large part in their decline, and yet these survivors often come down into tea plantations and secondary woodland.

Amirantes, and Common Waxbills locally in inner Seychelles. The grey-headed Madagascar race of the Malagasy Turtle-dove has all but swamped the vinous-headed Seychelles race by interbreeding. On the other hand, the Grey-headed Lovebirds which were also naturalised from Madagascar early in the twentieth century, although very numerous by the 1930s, then decreased and finally disappeared in the 1970s.

Extinctions

Madagascar was the home of the elephantbirds, half-a-dozen or more species of large to huge flightless ostrich-like creatures known only from skeletal fossils and egg remains. The biggest stood 3 m tall and possibly weighed up to 450 kg (approaching half a ton). It was thus one of the largest recorded birds and probably the heaviest of all. The huge eggs of this biggest elephantbird – over 30 cm long and with a capacity of 8–10 litres – perhaps helped to create the legend in *A Thousand and One Nights* of the Rukh, or Roc, which carried off elephants to feed its young. Marco Polo was told that the Roc inhabited islands south of Madagascar.

Early habitat destruction and hunting probably caused the disappearance of the elephantbirds, though the largest one may just have hung on until about 1650: the sole evidence for that, however, was the existence then of well-preserved eggs.

Otherwise, the Snail-eating Coua is the only bird now regarded as having become extinct in Madagascar since 1600, and even that possibly still survives somewhere. Last supposedly identified in 1930 – and, before that, not for nearly a century – it was (or is) a secretive forest bird; only a few specimens are known. It is often difficult to be certain, except on small islands, that such species are extinct: the rediscovery after nearly 60 years, also since 1930, of the Madagascar Serpent-eagle (*see* **51**) illustrates this well. The other nine couas – all pigeon-sized, long-legged and brightly coloured – are likewise confined to Madagascar, where they form an endemic subfamily of cuckoos.

Apart from, possibly, the '*poule bleue*', which was evidently common on Mahé in the eighteenth century, Seychelles never had any such unusual birds as some of those of Madagascar and the Mascarenes. Indeed, even the *poule bleue* was in all probability a form of the Purple Swamphen.

The only two indigenous landbirds known to have become extinct in Seychelles, both probably in the last quarter of the nineteenth century, are considered distinctive races of species that still exist elsewhere. The Seychelles Green Parakeet lived on the three largest islands and was exterminated as a pest of maize; it is generally regarded as a race of the Alexandrine Parakeet of southern Asia. The Seychelles Chestnut-flanked White-eye was possibly confined to the island of Marianne, where deforestation was its downfall; it

56

SEYCHELLES BLACK PARADISE-FLYCATCHER
Terpsiphone corvina

A dozen paradise-flycatchers inhabit Africa to Japan; females are 20–25 cm long, males usually have an extra 10–25 cm of tail-streamers that float behind in flight. Most have black heads and are rufous to orange-brown above and pale below – the standard female pattern – but some Madagascan and Asiatic males are white with black heads. Mascarene males are short-tailed and very like the females. Seychelles males are all blue-black with blue bill and eye-rings. Formerly on four islands, now mainly on one, this species needs forest of Alexandrian laurel and Indian almond with marsh nearby. Felling and drainage are threats, but part of the population of under 100 is now in a reserve.

is usually considered to have been conspecific with the Chestnut-sided White-eye of Mayotte, in the Comoros. Thus, no endemic species is known to have been lost, though the Aldabra Brush-warbler has not been seen for years (*p.113*).

It is worth adding that Abbott's Booby, a small gannet now confined to Christmas Island (*chapter 6*), used also to breed on Assumption, just south of Aldabra itself. Indeed, it was here that Abbott collected the original specimen. The species was wiped out soon after guano-quarrying began in 1908.

Probably no other islands in historic times had such a bizarre avifauna as the Mascarenes. In 250 years Man did more irreversible damage there more quickly and more thoroughly than anywhere else in the world, with the possible exception of the Hawaiian Islands (*chapter 8*). About a quarter each of the world's known bird extinctions since 1600 have been on small islands in the western Indian Ocean and tropical Pacific. In the Mascarenes, over 20 species were wiped out from the mid seventeenth century onwards, and these included some remarkable creatures.

Above all, Mauritius was the home of the Dodo, that most famous of all extinct birds. The cliché 'As dead as a Dodo' is familiar to many who have never heard of Passenger Pigeons or Great Auks, though some probably do not realise that such an extraordinary-looking bird really existed. Belonging to a now lost Mascarene family probably derived from pigeons and exhibiting the gigantism and flightlessness that are prone to evolve on isolated islands, it was greyish and turkey-sized but weighed over 20 kg (the baggage allowance for air travel now). It was regarded as stupid – for which a Portuguese word is 'doudo' – because of its vulnerability, tameness and clumsy appearance, with a disproportionately large head, huge hooked bill and absurd little curly white tail and rudimentary wings.

The other two Mascarene islands held related but less well-known flightless species, the Réunion and Rodrigues Solitaires (no relation whatsoever of the New World thrushes of that name). These were similar in size to the Dodo, but whitish and brown respectively and not so grotesque; the Réunion bird evidently lacked the curly tail and had a less peculiar bill.

The Dodo was wiped out by about 1662; the Réunion Solitaire hung on to at least 1715 and the Rodrigues bird until about 1761. All were slaughtered for food by visiting sailors, but the ultimate causes of extinction may have been egg-predation from introduced rats, cats, pigs and monkeys, and possibly also fires. This all serves to emphasise that, even in these more enlightened days when Man does not quite so readily try to destroy his fellow creatures, he can still do untold damage by thoughtless introductions and habitat destruction.

But the dodo family was not the only loss from the Mascarenes. Another half-dozen endemic species are known from specimens, and twice as many from subfossil bones and descriptions. If many of the names in the following list sound rather ordinary, it must be realised that some of these birds were remarkable enough to represent extinct genera rather than just individual species. Several of them had also lost the power of flight.

57

MAURITIUS PARAKEET
Psittacula eques

This is one of a dozen mostly Indomalayan parakeets that are basically green with some red or pink on shoulders, head, bill or breast and, in several cases, a rosy collar. The only indigenous one left in the Indian Ocean, it has been reduced to a handful by deforestation, hunting, and predation or competition from introduced monkeys and birds. Among the latter are Ring-necked Parakeets, widespread in Africa and south Asia; they differ in behaviour and ecology. Like certain other parakeets exterminated earlier on Réunion, Rodrigues and Seychelles, the endangered Mauritius bird is thought to have evolved from ancestors of the larger Alexandrine Parakeet of south-east Asia.

These further extinct endemics included a flightless ibis and a coot on Réunion; one or two possibly flightless night-herons, two flightless rails, two blue pigeons, and two owls on Mauritius and Rodrigues; a shelduck on Mauritius, and another duck there and on Réunion; two starlings on Réunion and Rodrigues; and at least four parrots (one flightless on Mauritius). These died out mainly during 1680–1700 (mostly Mauritius), in about 1725–26, and during 1761–73 (mostly Rodrigues), though four survived until the nineteenth century (two on Réunion).

Among yet other evident extinctions, of species inadequately defined, were a falcon, a large gallinule, a blue pigeon, a parrot and a fody on Réunion; an owl both there and on Mauritius; and a bulbul and a babbler on Rodrigues. The endangered Pink Pigeon of Mauritius (*see* **62**), or perhaps a similar species, apparently extended to Réunion.

Threatened birds

Madagascar's interesting avifauna, and its many other animals and plants, are threatened by pollution, wetland drainage, shooting and, above all,

---

58
RODRIGUES FODY
Foudia flavicans

*Most weaverbirds are African; fodies are a distinctive Malagasy group. The Madagascar Fody is widespread, having also been introduced north to Seychelles and east to Rodrigues; the Red-headed is common in east Madagascar, Comoros and Aldabra. But the Seychelles Fody is only on three islands; the Mauritius and the Rodrigues are endangered; and the Réunion is extinct. Fodies look sparrow-like until the males assume a red or yellow breeding plumage: the Rodrigues male has a yellow head and breast, and redder face. This once abundant species lost out to felling and cyclones (see **61**); the hundred or two survivors suffer competition from introduced Madagascar Fodies and predation from rats.*

---

continuing deforestation and other habitat destruction. Even if small in total number, this is a highly distinctive and important conglomeration of species.

Four Madagascan birds are already classed as 'Endangered', two of them aquatic species known chiefly from Lake Alaotra. The rare Alaotra Grebe (*see under* **52**) is threatened by hybridisation with rapidly colonising Little Grebes and by shooting for specimens. The even rarer Madagascar Pochard is hunted for food and sport. In addition, both suffer from loss of habitat to rice-growing and conflict with fishing interests: introduced tilapia compete directly for food and introduced bass prey on chicks and ducklings.

The two others 'Endangered' are birds of prey, the Madagascar Serpent-eagle (**51**) and the Madagascar Fish-eagle. Smaller, shorter-winged, longer-tailed and less strikingly marked than its African counterpart, but no less noisy, the fish-eagle is thought to be reduced to a mere 100 or so and threatened mainly by shooting.

Even if only these four species are currently 'Endangered', another 24 are classed as 'Vulnerable' or 'Rare', or at least suspected of being at risk. Five are wetland birds: the Madagascar Grebe (**52**) with much the same problems as the Alaotra; the Madagascar Heron and the Madagascar Teal (hunting, taking of eggs); and two rails, the Slender-billed Pygmy Crake and the black Sakalava Rail (drainage, rice-growing, netting).

The Madagascar Plover of coastal grassland and saltwater pools is also rare and declining, perhaps because of competition with a more recent colonist from Africa, Kittlitz's Plover. And Benson's Rock-thrush appears to be confined to dry rocky slopes in the south-west.

The remaining 17 threatened species are all forest or scrub birds losing their habitats. They include several from the endemic families described earlier: the three mesites (all to some extent also at risk from introduced rats, cats and dogs); four of the five ground-rollers (though some or all of these may still be less rare than previously thought); the Yellow-bellied Sunbird-asity; and Van Dam's Vanga and Pollen's Vanga.

59

RÉUNION CUCKOO-SHRIKE

Coracina newtoni

*The 70-odd arboreal and insectivorous cuckoo-
shrikes of the Old World tropics – a little like shrikes,
some grey and barred like certain cuckoos, but
related to neither – vary from 15 to 40 cm in length.
Half are island species; this and one on Mauritius are
among the most vulnerable. Both are down to a
hundred or two pairs under threat from introduced
animals: on Réunion, deer overgrazing in limited
habitat; on Mauritius, nest-raiding monkeys and rats,
and competing bulbuls and mynahs. Trapping and
tourism are additional pressures. Both males are grey
and white with black cap, wings and tail, but the
browner females differ below: Mauritius plain
orange-brown, Réunion white and barred.*

Others are the Madagascar Red Owl (**53**); at least
three of Madagascar's six greenbuls (a name used for a
number of mainly olive-green African and Malagasy
bulbuls); the Yellow-browed Oxylabes (one of an
endemic genus of rainforest babblers, heavily collected
for specimens around the turn of the century); and the
Red-tailed Newtonia (a tree-canopy warbler, known
from just one 1930 specimen until rediscovered at two
new sites in 1989–90).

So many more of Madagascar's birds are forest
species that this threatened list will grow if the forest
continues to be cut. Elsewhere in the world, a few
forest passerines have learnt to adapt to environments
greatly changed by Man; most cannot.

Of the 106 bird species endemic to Madagascar
alone, four-fifths occur in the eastern forest (including
20 of those at risk) and 30 are confined to that area. As
things stand, a quarter of the endemic birds are
considered to be threatened; this figure could rise to 40
per cent if all the forest goes.

Turning to the Comoros, five rare species there are
causing concern. Four of them on Gran Comoro – in
various specialised forest and scrub habitats on and
around Mount Karthala – are the Comoro Scops-owl,
Humblot's Flycatcher, Karthala White-eye and Gran
Comoro Drongo. The forest is under some threat from
roadbuilding and disturbance, and Mount Karthala
itself is still active, with three eruptions since the 1850s.
The fifth threatened species, the Mayotte Drongo, is
confined to degraded forest on Mayotte. Drongos in
general are black, though one of the Comoro species
has rusty-brown wings and tail, and are mainly
insectivorous with flycatching habits; they will also rob
other birds of food and are aggressive towards
predators.

Seychelles (down to Aldabra) and the Mascarenes
hold a variety of threatened landbirds. They and other
Indian Ocean islands, particularly towards Antarctica,
also have important seabird colonies. At present the
only seabird classed as 'Endangered' is the Amsterdam
Albatross (**54**), but the Kerguelen Tern is also causing

concern: one of the world's rarest terns, it has small colonies on Prince Edward and Crozet Islands, as well as on Kerguelen itself (*chapter 8*).

Just one of Aldabra's dozen landbirds – one of the two endemics – is at present threatened, although introduced cats and rats there prey on any small birds and introduced goats damage the vegetation. That is the critically endangered Aldabra Brush-warbler, which may already be extinct. Discovered only 25 years ago,

it has not been noted since the 1970s and the possible habitat is less than 50 ha.

If this sounds a small world range for a species, it may be added that some of the 11 endemics of the granitic Seychelles are confined to areas of comparable size. Three there are likewise classed as 'Endangered'. The Seychelles Magpie-robin, glossy black with white wing-patches, is another of the world's rarest birds. Formerly on several of the islands, this terrestrial and confiding species was an easy victim for introduced cats. Before they were removed, increasing numbers of feral cats on Frégate in the early 1980s halved the then population of around 40. Now there are about 25 on this one small island. Apart from the essential requirement of an absence of cats, this magpie-robin has special needs for its feeding areas and nest-sites; it suffers from food shortages and competition with the introduced Common Mynahs. A conservation programme by the RSPB and ICBP aims now to build up the numbers and reintroduce the species to a second island.

The other two seriously endangered birds are not so much commoner. The Seychelles Grey White-eye (**55**) is now restricted to three mountain areas on Mahé and,

60
MAURITIUS BLACK BULBUL
Hypsipetes olivaceus

Of over 120 bulbuls in Africa and tropical Asia, five are 'black': one widespread from Madagascar to China and each of the others endemic to one of four small Indian Ocean island groups – Nicobar, Seychelles, Réunion and Mauritius. About 25 cm long, these range from all-black to grey-brown, and greyer or greener below, with scruffy blacker crowns; bills and feet are red to orange-yellow. All are forest species with harsh nasal squawks, whistles and chatters. This one used to be among the commonest of Mauritius's endemics, but was already scarce by the early twentieth century. Tree clearance, cyclones and introduced predators and competitors have all acted against Mascarene birds (57–62, esp. 61).

61

THREATS TO ISLAND PIGEONS, AND THE MAURITIUS PINK PIGEON

Nesoenas mayeri

The pigeons are a large and very varied family of over 300 species. The smallest is lark-sized; the largest – the crowned pigeons of New Guinea (**84**) – are almost as big as female turkeys. All are plump with smallish heads, but their tails vary considerably in length and shape. Many are not particularly colourful, but some, such as the various green pigeons, certainly are. Most have characteristically cooing calls, though others utter harsher or more whistling notes.

Pigeons occupy a wide variety of habitats from subdesert and sea-cliffs to dense forest and cultivation. Since they all feed mainly on seeds, berries, flowers and shoots, many that live in agricultural areas have come to be regarded as pests. But those are among the more successful and adaptable; others, particularly forest species and ground-nesters, are much more vulnerable.

Most pigeons are strong fliers and some are great travellers that have colonised many of the world's islands, there evolving into new species; indeed, two-thirds of the world's pigeons are endemic to islands. Island birds in general have suffered greatly from Man's ruthlessness and carelessness. All but one of the half-dozen pigeons extinct since 1600 were island species, as are no less than 38 of the 50-odd currently at some risk or actually classed as 'Endangered'.

As it happens, the Malagasy region now has only seven endemic pigeons – a surprisingly small number compared with, say, Indonesia or certain Pacific archipelagos – but they include several of great interest. In particular, the blue pigeons, mostly dark blue and white with some bare red skin on the head, are a good example of a genus that is peculiar to islands. There were originally five of these striking species, but the Rodrigues and Mauritius Blue Pigeons have long been extinct.

The Mauritius Pink Pigeon is still hanging on 160 years after the extinction of the Mauritius Blue, but it has been a close thing. This is a large and fairly bulky, round-winged pigeon that is sometimes placed in the same genus as the various wood pigeons. It is, however, predominantly a beautiful pale pink, grading into whitish on the head, with dark brown mantle and wings, pink-brown lower back and rump, and rusty-brown tail with whitish outermost feathers.

The Pink Pigeon is a forest bird suffering from habitat loss, human persecution, and probably predation from introduced monkeys. Because its habitat has been so reduced, it is also at risk from cyclones. Winds up to 250 kph blow down nests, strip trees of the shoots and fruits on which the pigeons feed, and even drive birds out to sea. Cyclone Carol of February 1960 may have killed at least half of all the Pink Pigeons; almost as destructive were others in 1975 and 1979. Owing to earlier felling of large sections of forest, the remnant population has for many years been confined to a small area in the island's south-west, centred on a grove of introduced Japanese cedars.

Only 10–20 birds were left in the early 1980s, but by then a captive-breeding programme had been started with a view to reintroduction. The Mauritius government and zoos in the UK (Jersey Wildlife Preservation Trust), Germany and USA are playing important parts. This rescue programme came only just in time: a few years more and the Mauritius Pink Pigeon would probably have gone the way of its only close relative, the long extinct Pink Pigeon of Réunion.

apart from an isolated pocket on adjacent Praslin, the Black Paradise-flycatcher (**56**) is confined to La Digue. The populations of both are probably less than 100. The same ceiling figure applies to the Black Parrot – actually dark grey-brown – which in Seychelles is found only on Praslin, but this bird is shared with the Comoros and Madagascar, where it is abundant; thus, as a species, it is not threatened.

Five other Seychelles endemics are usually classed as 'Rare' or 'Vulnerable'. At one time the tiny Seychelles Kestrel, smallest of all typical falcons, was thought to be in a parlous state, but there are now over 300 pairs on Mahé, 50 on Silhouette and, following reintroduction, an increasing number on Praslin. The Seychelles Scops-owl, confined to Mahé and long believed extinct, has at least 75 pairs. The Seychelles Swiftlet, related to the Edible-nest Swiftlet of south-east Asia, may number over 1000, and is common on Mahé, Praslin and La Digue, but nests are in tight colonies in a few caves and so at risk from disturbance. The Seychelles Brush-warbler, superficially like the Common Reed-warbler of western Eurasia, was at one time reduced to no more than 50 on tiny Cousin Island, but

with habitat management increased to 300 and has now been introduced to Aride. Lastly, the Seychelles Fody, a dull-coloured weaver, is generally classed as 'Rare' but only because it is confined to three small cat-free islands; there the total population may number two or three thousands.

Four centuries ago the Mascarenes probably held over 40 endemic birds. Now only 15 or 16 remain, a mere four or five of them in reasonable numbers. Seven are 'Endangered' and five of those are hanging on by their wing-tips. The rare and little-known Mascarene Petrel perhaps used to nest also on Rodrigues, but is thought now to breed only in the mountains of Réunion. The Mauritius Parakeet (**57**), formerly also on Réunion, faces competition for nest-holes from the introduced and highly successful Ring-necked Parakeet; less than a dozen remain.

The Rodrigues Brush-warbler numbers less than 50, but could doubtless be increased by habitat-management and protection, as has the related species in Seychelles. Both the Rodrigues Fody (**58**) and the Mauritius Fody have declined dramatically to two or three hundred apiece during the twentieth century through habitat destruction, the subsequent effects of cyclones, competition with introduced Madagascar Fodies and, especially, the predations of introduced mammals. The Réunion and Mauritius Cuckoo-shrikes (**59**), the Mauritius Black Bulbul (**60**) and the Mauritius Olive White-eye are all in such small numbers or restricted habitat as to be classed as 'Vulnerable'.

On a happier note, two other 'Endangered' species, the Mauritius Pink Pigeon (**61**) and the Mauritius Kestrel (**62**), although at one time reduced to less than 20 and about six respectively, are now being bred in captivity by various zoos and released back to the wild. Such captive-breeding exercises may help to make up for the extent to which island birds, so long free of ground-predators and competitors in undisturbed habitats, have suffered from Man's interference in the last few centuries (*see also chapter 8*).

62

MAURITIUS KESTREL

Falco punctatus

*Conservation has its successes. By 1974, deforestation, persecution, cyclones, introduced predators and – probably most importantly – DDT spraying had reduced this small falcon to just six; 15 years later, with captive-breeding and releases (see **2**), there were over 70. Four of the world's 13 kestrels live in the Malagasy region. Both sexes of the Mauritius Kestrel look female: chestnut and whitish, all streaked, barred and spotted. In contrast, both in Seychelles have a male plumage: grey and rufous, spotted above (not barred) and plain below. Madagascar holds the other two species: the widespread Spotted Kestrel of open country and towns, and the atypical Banded Kestrel of forest.*

India and south-east Asia
through western Indonesia

Originally the 'Indian', and long the 'Oriental', this region is not confined to India, nor does it include Japan or most of China, two specifically Oriental countries. 'Indomalayan' is more appropriate for an area that, in addition to India, covers south-east Asia and many islands of Malaysia and Indonesia.

Barely larger than the Australasian (*chapter 7*), the Indomalayan region totals only about 9·5 million square km. Yet this relatively small area has almost 1860 indigenous breeding species, of which nearly 1400 are endemic. Regular migrants take the total well past 2000. These figures are high in proportion to those of the other tropical regions, when one realises that the landmass is not much more than half the size of South America, and less than a third of that of Africa.

The percentage of endemic birds is also high, especially as this is the one continental region sandwiched between two others – the Palearctic and the Australasian – and separated only by the Gulf of Oman from a third, the Afrotropical, with which it has strong affinities. In fact, the large number of continental islands makes the difference: many of the endemics are island forms. Though the triangle between Burma, Vietnam and peninsular Malaysia accounts for over 20 per cent of the land, and the Indian subcontinent 45 per cent, there are under 50 and only about 175 birds endemic to those areas.

The western boundary takes in lowland Pakistan north as far as the ridge of the Himalayas. That great mountain range – including most of the world's dozen highest peaks – forms an effective barrier against much of Palearctic Asia. Eastwards, in south China, the northern limit is the Chang Jiang (Yangtze), third

longest of all rivers. South and east of the continental landmass, the region includes many such islands as the Laccadives, Maldives, Sri Lanka, Andamans, Nicobars, Sumatra, Java, Lesser Sundas, Sulawesi (Celebes), Borneo, Philippines, Hainan and Taiwan.

The area known as Wallacea – the Indonesian islands eastwards from Sulawesi and, in the Lesser Sundas, Lombok – is transitional with the Australasian region. A clear dividing line – Wallace's Line – between Borneo and Sulawesi and, more strikingly, between Bali and Lombok is often treated as the boundary between the regions. For example, although the last two islands are no more than 30 km apart, the Indomalayan barbets and woodpeckers more or less stop at Bali, while the Australasian cockatoos and honeyeaters begin at Lombok. But the two faunas are more in balance farther to the east, between Sula and the Moluccas and, in the Lesser Sundas, between Babar and Tanimbar.

The boundary here is taken as the latter. Farther north, it also includes the Nansei-shotō (Ryūkyū Islands), south-west of Japan and east of China, which are transitional with the east Palearctic. Down in the Indian Ocean, just south of the equator, the tiny Chagos Archipelago is on the Maldive Ridge, and it is also convenient to take in here the Australian Cocos (Keeling) and Christmas Islands.

Large areas of the region's mainland are low-lying and, apart from the bounding Himalayas, almost no peaks exceed 4000 m. But, in addition to the Chang Jiang, this small continental region includes all or parts of five more of the world's top 40 rivers over 2500 km long: the Mekong, Indus, Salween, Brahmaputra and

Ganges, whose drainage basins cover hundreds of thousands of square kilometres. There are relatively few really large freshwater lakes, but many small ones; some low parts are periodically flooded by snowmelt, rain or, in the deltas, wind-swept seas. Borneo and Sumatra, respectively nearly three times and over twice the size of Britain, are the world's third and fifth largest islands.

Spanning about 45 degrees between 34°N and 11°S, the region is entirely tropical apart from northern India through south China. Except in the mountains, this northern section is mostly subtropical, 5–15°C in January and 25–35°C in July, in terrain that varies from desert in north-western India through scrub and steppe to rapidly disappearing humid and dry forest, which is coniferous on the Himalayan and other mountain slopes.

63

CABOT'S TRAGOPAN
Tragopan caboti

*Again arboreal (see **64**), and endangered from felling and hunting, Cabot's inhabits wet mountain forest, or bamboo and ferns, in south-east China. Two-thirds of a metre long, the male has a bare orange face, pale blue horns and throat (hidden here by the patterned lappet), and orange-red crest, neck-sides and throat-border. In display he stands upright with crest raised, the blue on the lappet obvious, the red and black thighs fluffed out; side-on to the female, he lowers the near wing, raises the other shoulder and spreads his tail to show the buff, black and red spots on his back, then circles around or, facing her, fluffs out with half-spread wings and shakes his head – horns and lappet erected.*

64

COLOURFUL AND THREATENED PHEASANTS, AND THE WESTERN TRAGOPAN

Tragopan melanocephalus

The pheasant family includes all the partridges and Old World Quails, where the sexes are either similar or, if different, not usually strikingly so apart from head-markings (some forest partridges and certain quails are exceptions). The pheasants proper – among them the four junglefowls, ancestors of domestic chickens, and the three peafowls (**67** *and* **43**) – are characterised by large size and generally colourful or strongly patterned male plumages with, in particular, a tendency to crests and broad or long and pointed tails.

This superbly coloured Western Tragopan is one example. Bare skin is red on the face and, not always obvious, blue on the throat; the otherwise black head is set off by red tips to the crest and a red neck; the rest is mainly grey-buff above and black below, variously barred and streaked, and conspicuously white-spotted. The much duller and – as is typical of most pheasants – considerably smaller female is, in general, grey with irregular streaks and spots.

Tragopans are also called 'horned pheasants' for the males' fleshy horns and wattle erected in displays that follow the pattern of those of pheasants in general (*see* **63**). Tragopans are highly arboreal, and unique among pheasants in that they build stick nests well up in trees; their chicks hatch with developed wing-feathers and, capable of very early flight, can thus roost with their mother in the trees.

With the notable exception of the African Peafowl (**43**), all the nearly 50 species of pheasants are Asiatic, the majority on the Indomalayan mainland north into the Himalayas. Most are forest birds, often living high in mountains. Many have long been kept and bred in captivity, and ten have been introduced to other continents with varying success. Best known is the Common or Ring-necked Pheasant, now widespread ferally over much of the northern hemisphere, as well as in New Zealand and southern Australia.

Three genera with relatively short-tailed males are mountain-forest birds of the Himalayas and China. These include the mop-crested Blood Pheasant, shaped like a large colourful partridge; the five tragopans, with particularly broad but dark or plain tails; and the three monals (**32**), with thin or bushy crests and rufous tails.

Males in the next group have medium-length tails, either drooping or arching, with broad or sickle-shaped feathers. All three eared pheasants (**66**), unique in that the sexes are similar, have feathery side-horns and broad tails with drooping plume-like central feathers; they are mainly Chinese mountain species of forest edge and barer highlands. The gallopheasants or 'firebacks', including the Kalij and Silver Pheasants, have a variety of crests and broad arching tail-feathers. Some have tails similar in shape and length to those of their nearest relatives, the combed and lappeted junglefowls. The ten firebacks and the four junglefowls are hill and lowland forest species up to 2000 m, mainly in south-east Asia and India.

The shortish-tailed Koklas Pheasant and the long-tailed Cheer (**65**) have pointed tails and strong backward crests. Both these mountain-scrub species of the Himalayas or China have relatively sombre

colours. Not so most of the remaining males with long pointed tails: the Common and Green Pheasants; the five 'barred-backs', including Hume's and Reeves's; and the particularly colourful and 'cowled' Golden and Lady Amherst's, also known as 'ruffed pheasants'. Apart from the last two, which live in dense mountain scrub, these are birds of light woodland and patchy scrub in open country at various altitudes, mostly in Palearctic Asia.

Finally, the six smallish but long-tailed peacock-pheasants of south China to Sumatra, and the two larger and excessively long-tailed arguses of Vietnam and Malaysia, provide links between typical pheasants and peacocks: although sombrely coloured in browns, greys, buffs and rufous, all the males have tail-spots equivalent to 'peacock eyes'. The peacock-pheasants actually have metallic-looking 'eye-spots' that extend to the wings too, while the Great Argus's main feature is its greatly elongated and spotted secondary flight-feathers two-thirds the length of the very long tail. These, again, are mainly forest birds of up to 2000 m.

There is general concern about the futures of many of the pheasants in China, India and south-east Asia. Over half are at risk: six are already classed as 'Endangered', eight as 'Vulnerable' and four as 'Rare'. Forest destruction, above all, threatens survival in the wild and, although many pheasants are legally protected, they are still hunted for food and collected for zoos or museums. Most are not difficult to breed in captivity: the answer must be to restock reserves and national parks when these are properly safeguarded.

65
CHEER PHEASANT
Catreus wallichi

*The Cheer, so named from its loud call, has a
standard long-tailed pheasant shape, but with a
narrow backward crest of hair-like feathers. Apart
from black crown, bare red face and dusky-centred
breast, males are buff, rufous and grey barred with
black; females are more chestnut below. Thus
cryptically coloured, they skulk in long grass and
scrub on broken slopes with scattered trees and
wooded gulleys up to 3500 m in the west Himalayas:
parties dig for tubers, bulbs and grubs, becoming
almost hidden in holes maybe 30 cm deep. The
species is now generally endangered by grazing,
burning and hunting, and even extinct in Pakistan;
captive-bred releases are being tried.*

Much of India is naturally steppe and savannah with
tropical forest in the south-west and north-east; rainforest also covered large parts of south-east Asia and
the islands, but much has already gone, particularly in
the Philippines. Except on higher ground, temperatures in most of this tropical zone remain above
20–25°C throughout the year.

Indigenous birds

For its size, as we have seen, the Indomalayan region
is proportionally the richest in birds: about one-
fifth of the world's species breeding on one-fifteenth of
the world's landmass. It also has a high measure at risk:
of some 1400 endemics, no less than 17 per cent are
causing concern.

Despite the long boundary with the Palearctic, and
the Australasian influence in the south-eastern islands,
the Indomalayan region's closest affinities are, in many
ways, with the Afrotropical. Almost all the bird
families of Africa – other than the endemics – are
represented in India and south-east Asia, though
sometimes in very different proportions.

A few families, indeed, are shared exclusively with
the Afrotropical region. The Spotted Creeper, for
example, sufficiently distinctive in structure to be
placed traditionally in a family of its own, is found only
in India and sub-Saharan Africa; it is not unlike a
blotchy treecreeper, but has an unstiffened, square tail.
Honeyguides are primarily African (*p.86*), but two are
Indomalayan: the Yellow-rumped up to about 2500 m
in the Himalayas, and the Malaysian from south-west
Thailand to Sumatra and Borneo. Conversely, while
four of the 14 broadbills are African, the ranges of all
the other ten are from the Himalayas and southern
China to the Philippines, Borneo and Java: chunky,
big-headed, mostly short-tailed and often colourful,
these slow-moving and secretive but nevertheless noisy
birds live mostly in forest, feeding on insects or, in
some cases, fruits.

Among several larger families or subfamilies mainly
confined to the Afrotropics and Indomalaya are the

hornbills (*see* **74**), barbets (*see* **22**), pittas (*see* **77**), cuckoo-shrikes (*see* **59** *and* **38**), bulbuls, babblers, sunbirds (*see* **45**), drongos, and weavers. For example, apart from one of four in Wallacea that extends to the Solomon Islands, the world's 48 hornbills are almost equally divided between the two regions. And, except for the few in the Malagasy region, and a handful that reach marginally into the Palearctic region, the 120 bulbuls are more or less similarly divided.

The weavers, on the other hand, are a predominantly African family of 105 species, of which a few live in the Malagasy region (*see* **58**) and just five between India and Java. The sunbirds, too, though distributed from Africa to Australia and occurring in all the main Old World regions, have less than 40 species in Indomalaya, half as many as in the Afrotropics. The total of 25 Indomalayan barbets is also not much more

66
WHITE EARED PHEASANT
Crossoptilon crossoptilon

The only pheasants with the sexes similar, the three 'eared' species are big and bulky; long ear-coverts form small horns, and broad tails have elongated central feathers with soft drooping basal webs like ostrich plumes. All are Chinese; this one extends to Tibet and Assam. White only in the east and centre of its range, it is pale grey in the north and dark blue-slate in the west. Its crown is usually black, its flight-feathers dark and its tail bronze through green-blue to purple. Legs and face are always red, and throat, 'ears' and nape-band white. Once common at 3–5000 m in rhododendron and juniper scrub – eating shoots, bulbs and berries – it is under threat from felling and hunting.

67

GREEN PEAFOWL
Pavo muticus

'Peacocks' of zoos and estates are usually Indian Peafowl, still wild where protected in India and Sri Lanka. The Green Peafowl, once common in south-east Asia, has gone from Bangladesh and Assam, and is now rare in much of its range from Burma and south China to Malaysia; it hangs on in reserves and on islands. Of similar size, both males have long ocellated trains. But, against the Indian's wire-like fan-crest topped with discs, white face, blue neck and barred wings, this greener bird has a pointed crest, blue and yellow face, dark-spotted neck of dull green-gold, and glossed wings. Inhabiting forest or elephant grass, often by streams or paddies, it is vulnerable to felling and hunting.

than half as many as in Africa though they, like the 13 South American species (*see* **22**), are generally larger and more colourful than their African counterparts; the three groups are now proposed as separate families. Conversely again, there are nearly four times as many cuckoo-shrikes (including minivets) and drongos in the Indomalayan region, over six times as many babblers (nearly 200), and over ten times as many pittas (though only 22 in all).

Similarly, while many of the more cosmopolitan families are shared fairly equally between the two regions, some are far more strongly represented in one or the other. India and south-east Asia have considerably more herons and bitterns, ducks, owls, kingfishers, white-eyes, and finches than Africa – half as many again in some cases. And they have at least twice

as many pigeons, parrots, cuckoos and woodpeckers; four times as many crows; and no fewer than 11 trogons compared with just three – though even that is under half as many as in Central and South America (*see* **9** *and* **21**). Above all, the Indomalayan region has more than three-quarters of the world's 48 pheasants (*see* **64**), in striking contrast to Africa's one (**43**).

On the other hand, Africa has many more bustards, sandgrouse, nightjars, bee-eaters, rollers, larks, swallows, pipits, warblers, penduline-tits, waxbills and mannakins, and starlings. And Indomalaya lacks guineafowls, turacos, wood-hoopoes, helmet-shrikes, bush-shrikes, and so on. Both regions have two or three jacanas, and the same painted-snipe, Crab-plover, Avocet, Black-winged Stilt and Oystercatcher, as well as one darter, finfoot and skimmer apiece.

68

MALEO

Macrocephalon maleo

This is one of the scrubfowl that, with the larger Australasian Malleefowl and brush-turkeys, make up the megapode ('big foot') family. Some 50 cm long, it is unusual for the dark horny casque on its almost bare head, and for its white underbody often tinged with pink-buff. Endemic to Sulawesi (Celebes), the few thousands that remain belong to only about a dozen nesting groups largely restricted to the north peninsula and the south-east. Shy and living in hill forest up to 1200 m, they descend to beaches to bury their eggs, which are then incubated by the sun and volcanic heat from hot springs (p.157). Eggs are often taken by local people, so such a small population is very vulnerable.

69
GREAT INDIAN BUSTARD
Ardeotis nigriceps

The bustards – terrestrial with stout bodies and long necks and legs – are a family of over 20 Old World species; three are native to India. Larger than Europe's Great Bustard, this male is over a metre high; the female is also white and black with a finely marked sandy back, but duller and only three-quarters the size. The Great Indian Bustard lives in dry grassland with some scrub, and the half-sized Bengal and Lesser Floricans in richer grass – but much of India's grassland has yielded to cattle and cultivation. In the nineteenth century this big bird ranged over most of Pakistan and India, a common target for hunters. Today, probably under 1000 remain, only in the west-central states.

Of the high total of 95 indigenous bird families in the Indomalayan region, only two are endemic: the first figure is close to that of the Neotropics, the second very poor compared with any of the other tropical regions.

One endemic family traditionally includes the eight leafbirds and four ioras, all small to medium-sized passerines, and the two rather larger fairy-bluebirds. One of the last, which are fruit-eating forest birds, occurs from India to Java, the other in the Philippines only; males are brilliant shiny blue and black above, and all-black below. The forest leafbirds, which feed on insects, fruits and nectar, are mainly green, or green and yellow or orange, and males mostly have black and blue throats. The more exclusively insectivorous ioras, which are not now thought related to the leafbirds, are green above – or, in three cases, green and black with two white wing-bars – and yellow or green below; some extend into scrub country.

The two Philippine creepers are the other traditionally recognised endemic family. Forest birds, they do climb trunks, something like straight-billed treecreepers, but they feed mainly in the canopy.

The three or four crested tree-swifts – much less aerial and more strikingly patterned than typical swifts – are a primarily Indomalayan family that extends to the Solomon Islands. Similarly, three-quarters of the dozen large nightjar-like frogmouths are Indomalayan, the rest Australasian. Flowerpeckers – small, short-tailed, noisy, and somewhat like sunbirds in behaviour – are also shared only with Australasia: of nearly 50 species, two-thirds are Indomalayan.

This low extent of endemism at the family level is perhaps not surprising for a region sandwiched between two others and having close affinities with a third. Indeed, because of its position, Indomalaya includes a number of Palearctic and Australasian birds. But many of the Palearctic families represented – such as dippers, accentors, long-tailed tits, and treecreepers – are found only around the Himalayas, or just reach north Thailand and Laos, and so are hardly typical of Indomalaya. Several nuthatches, however, extend down into south-east Asia and one, the Velvet-fronted, as far as Sri Lanka, Java and the Philippines. Typically Sino-Himalayan, too, are the parrotbills though, again, there are a dozen in south-east Asia.

In the Indonesian and other islands, particularly the transition zone of Wallacea, the Australasian influence is marked. The Australo-Papuan megapodes are represented by the Maleo (*see* **68**) and three scrubfowls; and the logrunners and rail-babblers by the Malaysian Rail-babbler. The 50-odd whistlers or thickheads – the latter a reference to shape rather than intellectual capacity – are again typically Australo-Papuan, but include two species endemic to the Sundas, three to Sulawesi, and one each to Borneo and the Philippines, together with three more widespread west to, respectively, Sulawesi, Java and eastern India.

70

STORM'S STORK
Ciconia stormi

Almost 20 species of storks are represented in all continents, most in the Old World tropics: up to over a metre high, with long bills, necks and legs, short tails, long broad wings. The Woolly- or White-necked has a wide range from Africa and India to Indonesia: glossy black and white, with black skullcap, white neck (loosely feathered) and belly, reddish-black bill, bare black face, and red legs. Storm's Stork, now recognised as a distinct species, is slightly smaller, with red bill and face, and black foreneck. It has nested in Thailand, but is mainly confined to forested wetlands in Sumatra and Borneo; as the forests disappear, the larger and more catholic Woolly-necked takes its place.

Even more Australasian are the wood-swallows, and the large family of honeyeaters shared with the Pacific islands (*chapter 8*). Of the dozen or so wood-swallows – long-winged, graceful in flight, and insectivorous, but stocky, stout-billed and more closely related to crows than to swallows – three extend as far west as the Andamans or western Indonesia, and one is confined to India and south-east Asia. Only one of some 160 honeyeaters reaches as far west as Bali, but there are a dozen more in Wallacea.

Similarly of Australasian origin are two of the five cormorants breeding in the region – the Little Black and Little Pied – both as far west as Java. Apart from two gulls and more than a dozen terns, of which only the Black-bellied Tern is endemic, there are few other Indomalayan breeding seabirds, all of which are confined to islands of the eastern Indian Ocean and inshore western Pacific. They include three or four shearwaters and petrels, two tropicbirds, four boobies and three frigatebirds (*see* **76**).

Introductions

Naturalised birds are of little significance in much of Indomalaya. Indeed, mainland south-east Asia has no more than about a dozen artificially established species, mostly uncommon or local.

Islands are so often the worst sufferers but in this region, fortunately, the numbers of introductions are generally small there too: Sri Lanka and Taiwan have but one naturalised species each and, towards the higher end of the scale, Singapore and Hong Kong no more than eight apiece. Even the much larger Borneo and Philippines also hold no more than eight, while all the islands of Indonesia, from Sumatra to western New Guinea, muster only six certain introductions and another 11 that may be established locally. On the other hand, the tiny Chagos Archipelago, only 60 square km in extent, has some 16 alien birds breeding, while as many more have been tried and failed. Among these are all the species introduced to Seychelles, including Grey Francolins, and even Cattle Egrets.

71
GIANT IBIS
Pseudibis gigantea

Some ibises, like the White-faced in South America, are among the most abundant of larger waterbirds, but a quarter of the 25 species are under threat (see also **27–28**). *The Giant Ibis, biggest of all, was always scarce in undisturbed swamps and open forest in south-east Thailand and south Indochina, mainly by the Mekong and its tributaries, but it has now disappeared from most areas and may be extinct. Deforestation and the spread of rice and other agriculture, not to mention human strife and population problems, have taken their toll. This dark, red-legged ibis, greeny-grey-brown with bare brown head and neck barred laterally at the back, is hardly beautiful but its loss would be extremely sad.*

Turning back to the mainland, the birds most commonly introduced to other parts of the world were already indigenous somewhere in the Indomalayan region. Common Pheasants, for example, are indigenous in the north-east and, of course, there are many other pheasants in India and south-east Asia. Rock Pigeons, too, are indigenous to India and Sri Lanka, though there, and throughout much of at least the mainland, feral populations are a now familiar sight in towns, cultivation, and broken country.

House Sparrows are indigenous to the Indian subcontinent east to Burma, and have otherwise been introduced only to a few islands, such as the Andamans and the Chagos. This may partly be because the Tree Sparrow naturally fills the sparrow niche in south-east Asia down to Java and Bali; it, in turn, has been introduced to the Philippines, Borneo, Sulawesi, Lombok, and so on. That other great worldwide introduction, the Common Starling, is found in northern India, but not elsewhere: competition with the equally aggressive Common Mynah, here a native, may be too great.

Common Mynahs themselves are naturalised in various parts of the tropical and southern temperate Old World, particularly on oceanic islands and in New Zealand, Australia and South Africa: they are indigenous to much of mainland Indomalaya, but have been introduced to Hong Kong and parts of Malaysia. Three more mynahs of the region have also been introduced in such places as Hong Kong, Penang, Singapore and Luzon.

Other indigenous birds have increased ranges through introductions. The Barred Ground-dove, or Peaceful or Zebra Dove, whose natural range is from peninsular Burma to Australia, has been artificially spread to other parts of Thailand, and the Philippines and Chagos. Ring-necked Parakeets, indigenous to India and Burma, were introduced to Malaysia (but probably died out) and Hong Kong. House Crows were similarly established in Malaysia for insect control, and spread to Penang and Singapore.

Small seed-eaters are among the commonest introductions, in some cases through accidental escapes in a region which plays a huge part in the cagebird trade: for example, Green Munias in Lahore, White-headed Munias in Hong Kong, Red Avadavats in Malaysia and the Philippines, Javanese Mannikins and Nutmeg Mannikins in Singapore and, eaily the most widespread, Java Sparrows. The last were originally confined to Java and Bali, but are now naturalised in Sri Lanka and much of south-east Asia, as well as in the Philippines, Sulawesi, and various of the Sunda Islands.

In general, however, the impact of bird introductions on the Indomalayan avifauna is minute. They do not threaten any of the endemics that make up three-quarters of the region's breeding species.

Extinctions

The presumed extinctions in the Indomalayan region since 1600 fall into two categories: mainland birds that could just possibly still exist in inadequately explored regions, and island forms that have certainly or almost certainly gone.

Among the latter were the Silver-banded Black Pigeon (last recorded 1936) and the Miyako Kingfisher (1841), both from the Nansei-shotō (Ryūkū Islands); the Four-coloured Flowerpecker (1906), from the Philippine island of Cebu; and the little-known Rowley's Flycatcher, from the Indonesian island of Sangir. There have been only two records of the last: a single nineteenth-century specimen and a sighting in 1978, both relating to forest on an island where the forest has now all but gone.

Much the most famous of the probable mainland extinctions is the Pink-headed Duck, originally of north-east India to north Burma and just possibly still extant around the borders of Burma and Tibet. The last definite record was as far back as 1935, but there have been unconfirmed reports since. It is, or was, highly distinctive with blackish-brown throat, fore-neck and body, contrasting deep pink bill, head and neck, pale pink underwings. Unfortunately, though there used to be some in captivity, they died out in 1939 – well before the modern concept of releasing captive-bread stock back to the wild.

Although an island, Java is slightly larger than England and so it is hard to be certain that no Javanese Wattled Lapwings remain. This mainly blackish-brown plover with pendant creamy face-wattles and long yellowish legs has, however, not been seen since 1939. It used to inhabit open ground near freshwater pools and may have been a victim of agriculture and hunting.

The difficulties of being sure that a species is extinct are illustrated by another wader. The large and strikingly marked Jerdon's Courser, of rocky hills with light forest and scrub in south-east India, was thought extinct by 1900, then rediscovered in 1986: it had been missed because it is primarily nocturnal.

The Himalayan Mountain Quail, a small partridge rather than a quail, has not been recorded since 1868; and its limited range around 2000 m in the western Himalayas has been combed without success. The worry now must be for the 31 other quails, partridges and, particularly, pheasants (*see* **64**) that form a major group of the region's threatened birds.

Threatened birds

In the Indomalayan region, and in China as a whole, increasing human populations pose great threats: pollution and pesticides, illegal hunting and trapping for food or as cagebirds and, above all, deforestation, drainage and other habitat damage. The mass conversion of wetlands to rice paddies comes from a need to feed over half the world's people living on only one-twelfth of the land.

Also at risk are many of the hundreds of millions of central and eastern Palearctic birds that winter in the region: as elsewhere in the tropics, these include storks, raptors, terns, doves, cuckoos, nightjars, swifts, bee-eaters, rollers, and, especially, ducks and waders, as well as hordes of such passerines as swallows, pipits, chats and other thrushes, flycatchers, warblers, shrikes, and orioles.

Some 230 of the Indomalayan region's own birds are causing concern: about 12 per cent of the breeding species and one-sixth of all the endemics. Over 30 are quails, partridges and pheasants. Illustrated are the Cabot's and Western Tragopans (**63–64**) and Cheer Pheasant (**65**), all 'Endangered', and the White Eared Pheasant (**66**) and Green Peafowl (**67**), both 'Vulnerable'. Apart from hunting and other disturbance, many pheasants are unable to adapt to altered habitats, though Taiwan's endemic Mikado Pheasant is not doing badly in that respect: there are still some thousands in the central mountains.

In addition, one francolin, one wood-partridge, one quail and a third of the 18 almost exclusively Indomalayan 'hill-partridges' (not all of which are upland birds) have question marks hanging over them. Several are simply little known, or have tiny ranges, but others are clearly threatened by deforestation or cultivation.

All the region's four megapodes, an Australasian family (*p.157*), are also at risk, through deforestation and the taking of eggs for food. The Maleo (**68**) is the most colourful. The other three – on islands off Sulawesi, in the Philippines and, very isolated, in the Nicobars west of peninsular Thailand between Sumatra and the Andamans – are dull brownish birds.

India is the eastern limit for most bustards. Three were once common there, but the Great Indian Bustard (**69**) and the Lesser Florican are both now at dangerously low levels, through habitat loss as much as the once excessive hunting. The Bengal Florican – not unlike the Lesser, but bigger, with elongated crest-feathers and chest-plumes – is largely restricted to Nepal and north-east India to Assam, where only a few hundreds remain. Another population of uncertain origin used to spend much of the year in Cambodia, and a few reappeared in south Vietnam in the 1980s.

Many water or water-associated birds have been badly affected by habitat damage, pollution, hunting and war. The White-bellied Heron, one of the largest of all herons, lives in swamps and forest rivers between Nepal and former strongholds in the upper reaches of

Burma's Irrawaddy, but is now extremely rare. The much smaller White-eared Night-heron of very different but no less vulnerable habitat – mountain forest with bamboo thickets in Hainan and south-east China – may already be extinct; a close relative of the threatened Japanese Night-heron (*p.67*), it is named for the white stripe behind the eyes on its blackish head.

Storm's Stork (**70**) and the Giant Ibis (**71**) are enigmatic forest-dwellers that, despite their size, have proved difficult to find in recent years; indeed, the ibis is another that may now have gone. The Milky Stork, something like Europe's White Stork, has a rather larger range in Cambodia, south Vietnam, peninsular Malaysia, Sumatra and Java; but, though found in various lowland wetlands from marshes to mangroves, its total population may now be under 1000. Also

72
GREAT PHILIPPINE EAGLE
Pithecophaga jefferyi

A century ago there were 2000 or more of these huge brown and white eagles in the Philippines. Now only a hundred or two remain on just four of the larger islands. This endangered bird has become one of the world's 20 rarest raptors. Its forest home is going fast and, despite being the 'National Bird', it is still shot and trapped. Though spanning up to 2 m, it has the relatively short rounded wings that go with a life among trees; indeed, it flaps and glides like an enormous sparrowhawk, and has a longish tail as well. Its narrow, deep, arched bill and the bushy erectile crest on its dark-streaked, creamy head are distinctive; its massive feet can grasp monkeys and flying lemurs.

drastically depleted throughout its range from Burma to south Vietnam, and another casualty of war, has been the White-shouldered Ibis, which is closely related to north India's Black Ibis.

Even aquatic birds with wide Indomalayan ranges have seriously declined this century, especially in the last 30 years. The huge Greater Adjutant Stork, south-east Asia's answer to Africa's Marabou and just as ugly, was originally found from India to Vietnam, but the population has crashed: now Assam is the only part where small numbers survive as a protectable entity. Similarly, the Spot-billed Pelican, a southerly equivalent of the Dalmatian (*see* **25**), has declined over much of its range from India to Borneo, though at least until recently was still not uncommon in Sri Lanka; there the old reservoirs, or 'tanks', provide good habitats.

Shy forest waterbirds are at great risk. The White-winged Duck, blackish with white forewings and pepper-and-salt head, is related to South America's Muscovy so familiar in domesticated forms; a mainly nocturnal bird of humid forest pools, it was once widespread from north-east India to Java, but deforestation has reduced it to a few areas, mostly reserves, in

73
PHILIPPINE FOREST KINGFISHER
Ceyx melanurus

Most of the more than 90 species of kingfishers occur in the Old World tropics, but not all are associated with fish or water. Some live on insects and lizards in forest far from rivers and lakes. One such is this Philippine endemic, a small kingfisher that often perches high on trees. Already scarce, it is threatened by deforestation. It varies locally in colour tones, in the lengths of its wings, tail and scarlet bill, and in size (20 per cent larger on Samar and Leyte than on Luzon, for example). Its lilac-rufous plumage is offset by mainly black wings, a white throat and belly, yellow lores, a white patch on the neck-sides, and usually a blue spot above (though that is missing on Mindanao).

Assam, Bangladesh, north Burma, and Sumatra. The Masked Finfoot, another secretive waterbird with a similar range from Assam to Sumatra, now appears rare throughout what remains of its forest swamps and mangroves; this is the heavy-billed Asiatic representative of a longish-necked tropical trio that look like crosses between grebes and cormorants, but are allied more closely to cranes and rails.

Threatened forest landbirds include many raptors: adapted to life among trees and often to particular arboreal prey, they need undisturbed tracts of primary forest. Especially at risk are several island species in the south-east Asiatic complex of serpent-eagles, characterised by elongated heads, flattened crests, distinctive screams and, in flight, broad white bands on wings and tail. All live largely on snakes and lizards. Differing greatly in size and colour, they have been treated as anything from five species (and a number of well-marked races) to 13. Most of the island forms, except for the Sulawesi Serpent-eagle, appear now to have total numbers only in the low hundreds. Four are particularly threatened, each with a population of, probably, under 100. One is the Great Nicobar Serpent-eagle, endemic to Great Nicobar Island and actually the smallest of all; the other three are much paler birds on the central Nicobars and in the Nansei-shotō, and a dark one on Bawean Island, between Borneo and Java.

Among other threatened forest raptors are several endemic accipiters, such as the Nicobar Sparrowhawk and the Small Sparrowhawk of Sulawesi, both of which are thought to number only a few hundreds, and especially some of the hawk eagles, of which the Javan is the rarest and the Philippine the most threatened by deforestation. For the same reason the far larger Great Philippine Eagle (**72**) is among the world's most endangered raptors.

Nearly 20 pigeons, almost a third of the Indomalayan total, are also causing concern. South-east Asia's scarce Large Green Pigeon is, as its name suggests, the biggest of over 20 fruit-eating green pigeons that, apart from two in Africa, are mainly Indomalayan. Other fruit-eaters are the smallish, often colourful fruit-doves and the big imperial pigeons: the Indomalayan, Australasian and Pacific regions hold nearly 50 of the former and three dozen of the latter.

Several of each of these three large genera of pigeons – mostly forest birds and many of them island endemics of the Philippines and Lesser Sundas – are either threatened or hardly recorded for many years. Some big imperials have also been hunted to excess as tree clearance and roads have opened up their habitats: to none does this apply more than the Christmas Imperial, of Christmas Island, greatly reduced in numbers, already 'Vulnerable', and further threatened by phosphate-mining. Another group of pigeons, on islands east and south from the Philippines and out into the Pacific, are 15 or more of the ground-doves known as 'bleeding-hearts': four in the Philippines and Lesser Sundas are now rarely recorded.

Indomalayan wood pigeons are upland forest birds that have little in common in appearance or behaviour with their European counterpart. Four now scarce or threatened are the Sri Lanka Wood Pigeon; the Silver Wood Pigeon, of small west Indonesian islands; and two on the mainland, the Nilgiri of south-west India and the Pale-capped of south-east Asia.

Parrots suffer not only from deforestation, but also from the cagebird trade. A dozen Indomalayan species, several restricted to smaller islands, are at grave risk from one or both. Red-vented and Lesser Sulphur-crested Cockatoos, of the Philippines and Indonesia respectively, are the region's only representatives of an otherwise essentially Australasian group (*see* **82**). The Red-and-blue Lory, of the Sangir and Talaud Islands north of Sulawesi, and the five Philippine racket-tailed parakeets (others live in Sulawesi and Buru) are also threatened. It is not clear where the little-known Rothschild's Parakeet lives: odd ones appear in bird markets in northern India. Blyth's Parakeet is restricted to the Nicobars. The hanging-parrots are a group of about ten small fruit- and nectar-feeders, green with

patches of red, notably on the rump: two on the islands of Sangir and Flores must be at grave risk and the latter is known only from one specimen.

Nearly a third of the world's 140-odd cuckoos are Indomalayan, mostly in forest or dense woodland; the majority are not parasitic but build platform nests. At least five island species are causing concern. Two Sri Lankan specialities are declining with forest loss. The large Red-faced Malkoha keeps to the canopy; glossy blackish above, and white below the breast, it has a heavy green bill, large bare red cheek-patches, and broad white tips to long tail-feathers. The Green-billed Coucal needs bamboo undergrowth; black and chestnut, also with a large green bill, this is one of a separate family of large terrestrial cuckoos of the Old World tropics. Others are Steere's Coucal, endemic to the badly deforested Philippine island of Mindoro; and the Sunda Coucal, once ranging over much of Java but now confined to a single area. The Sunda Ground Cuckoo seems to have disappeared from Sumatra, but may still exist on Borneo.

The region is also rich in owls, with around a third of the world's 15 barn-owls (heart-shaped facial discs) and 160 typical owls (circular facial discs), but some are hardly known. There are only pre-1914 specimens of Blewitt's Forest Owl, a relative of Europe's Little Owl, and, similarly, just a few old (often nineteenth-century) specimens of several endemic scops-owls of the Philippines, Lesser Sundas, Java and Sumatra. Scops-owls are found worldwide, but many are hard to locate without knowing their calls. Even the larger, longer-tailed White-fronted Scops-owl of lowland forest in peninsular Burma, Thailand and Malaysia is little known, as is the still bigger Philippine Eagle-owl, endemic to disappearing mountain forest.

Other nocturnal birds are no less hard to assess, and their ranges are often restriced by special needs. The Kalabat Nightjar, of north Sulawesi, and Salvadori's Nightjar, of Sumatra and Java, are little-known mountain species in areas of deforestation. The frogmouths are an essentially Indomalayan and Australasian

74

HELMETED HORNBILL
Rhinoplax vigil

Hornbills, famed for their beaks and the female's practice of sealing herself into a nest-hole, live in Africa and south Asia, mostly in forest, though half the Africans are savannah birds. Seven of the 20 Indomalayan species are at risk from deforestation. One of the largest – with tail-streamers that help to give it the length of a man's outstretched arms – is this brown and white hornbill of Borneo, Sumatra and Malaysia north, just, to Thailand. Contrast is added by the yellow-tipped red bill and casque, bare red neck, white tail and, in flight, white wing-edges. Despite legal protection, it is hunted for its feathers and for the casque traditionally carved into ornaments.

BALI STARLING
Leucopsar rothschildi

*Over 100 starling species inhabit the Old World, most
in the tropics. Many live successfully with Man; this
one, known also as Rothschild's Mynah, is gravely
endangered. Always restricted to north coastal Bali,
east of Java, it was once common but now only a few
dozen remain. The striking plumage – all white but
for black-tipped wings and tail, and bare blue eye-
patches – have long targeted it as a cagebird.
Trapping goes on despite legal protection, and even
though it is easy to breed in aviaries: there are now
many times more worldwide in captivity than remain
in the wild. Black-winged Starlings, natives of Java,
Bali and Lombok and adaptable to human pressures,
also compete for nest-sites.*

family, superbly camouflaged like nightjars but with
larger bills, huge gapes and short rounded wings. Unlike the aerial-feeding, ground-nesting nightjars, they
take most prey – insects, scorpions, frogs, even mice –
on the ground by pouncing flights from branches,
and make simple nests on horizontal boughs. Six of the
dozen frogmouths extend to mainland India or south-
east Asia; three are restricted to the Philippines or
Indonesia: all are little known, but they too are forest
birds, often of areas where the trees are going fast.

The same applies to half-a-dozen little-known or
scarce kingfishers of lowland forest, wooded marshland, or mangrove in the Philippines and Lesser
Sundas: for example, the Philippine Forest Kingfisher
(**73**). The Red-collared Woodpecker – all green but for
a red collar, nape and (male only) crown – is scarce on

the borders of south-west China and north Laos and Vietnam, another area where forest has suffered.

Many African hornbills are savannah birds, and the Indian Grey also lives in more open country, but most of the Asiatic half of the family are again confined to forests, even though some forage into adjacent scrub and cultivation. Larger hornbills, like the Helmeted (**74**) and Rufous-necked, are also hunted. Three hornbills have tiny ranges. The Narcondam and Sumba Hornbills are endemic to single islands in the Andamans and Lesser Sundas. The Sulu Hornbill inhabits the small south-western islands of the Philippines: everywhere in that country the forest is being ravaged and bigger birds are shot for food by hungry locals.

The forest devastation in the Philippines threatens passerines as well. The Wattled Broadbill and Koch's Pitta, endemic representatives of two characteristic Indomalayan families (*see p.122 and* **77**), are now apparently rare or very local. Half-a-dozen Philippine babblers – another family typical of the whole region – are also causing concern. So too are a couple of Philippine cuckoo-shrikes (*see also* **59** *and* **38**), the Black and White-winged Greybirds, which are both confined to one or two islands.

Some forest birds may be able to adapt to secondary growth. On Cebu, where virtually all the forest has been cut, the Black Shama – one of the smallish and, in several cases, long-tailed thrushes, also known as magpie-robins, that include some of the finest Indomalayan songsters – seems in fact to have done just that. And the little-known Mottle-breasted Bulbul belongs to a genus which, elsewhere, has also adapted. But one cannot hold out the same hope for several more Philippine forest birds that are already scarce and mostly restricted to one or two islands. These include two jungle flycatchers and two more, the Blue-breasted Niltava and Vaurie's Flycatcher; the Celestial and Short-crested Blue Monarchs (*see also* **100**–**101**); the longest-billed form of the Plain-headed Creeper, one of the two endemic Philippine creepers (*p.126*); and the Isabella Oriole.

Scarce endemic songbirds of other habitats in the Philippines include the Water Redstart of rocky mountain streams on Luzon; and the Green-faced and Red-eared Parrotfinches, small grassfinches endemic to Luzon and Mindanao respectively.

The next large islands to the south-west and south of the Philippines are Borneo and Sulawesi (Celebes). Borneo is now divided into four states: tiny independent Brunei; rather larger Sabah and Sarawak, forming part of Malaysia; and Kalimantan, the largest single landmass of Indonesia. A number of scarce endemic passerines in Borneo's forests include another lowland pitta, the Blue-headed; Everett's Ground-thrush, in the mountains of Sarawak and Sabah; two more babblers, the Black-browed (known only from one nineteenth-century specimen) and the lowland Borneo Wren-babbler; and the atypical Pygmy White-eye. Also the Blue-wattled Bulbul, shared only with Sumatra, and the Javan White-eye, shared only with Java, both with small known ranges.

Sulawesi has more forest birds at risk. These include several larger species, notably the Maleo (**68**) and two of that secretive family of rails that have suffered so much from habitat change and introduced predators on islands everywhere (*see p.153 and* **92**): both Platen's and Bald-faced Rails are little known but evidently rare. The Sulawesi Woodcock, not unlike the European but heavier-billed and most unmarked below, is confined to two areas of mountain forest.

Among Sulawesi's passerines, the Red-backed Ground-thrush, Heinrich's Mountain-thrush and the Sulawesi Jungle-flycatcher are scarce forest species. Other flycatchers, the Sulawesi Blue and Sanford's Niltava, are restricted to single areas of mountain forest.

Rowley's Flycatcher is endemic to Sangir, north of Sulawesi, but only tiny patches of forest are left there and it may already be extinct (*p.129*). Also dependent on Sangir's forest remnants are the Sangir Yellow-backed Sunbird and a distinctive race of the Rufous Shrike-thrush, which is a whistler (*p.127*), as well as the Sangir Hanging-parrot (*p.134*). On Banggai, to the east of Sulawesi, the Banggai Crow is known only from old specimens.

The Lesser Sundas from Lombok east to Damar and Babar – the southern side of Wallacea – are part of the zone of transition with the Australasian region (*p.118*). Some endemics of this island chain, such as the Orange-banded Ground-thrush, Black-banded Flycatcher and Spot-breasted White-eye – all mainly or entirely on Timor – are reported as uncommon, decreasing or restricted to forest remnants. The same applies to the Crested White-eye of Flores and Sumbawa. The Timor Sparrow, a grassfinch related to the Java Sparrow, is now found only in lowland scrub on Timor and Semau.

Other Lesser Sundan endemics are little known or, because some of these islands are hardly visited by ornithologists, have not even been recorded for half a century or more. Almost nothing is known, for example, about Hartert's Flycatcher or the Apricot-breasted Sunbird, both endemic to Sumba. The same applies to Everett's Monarch, of Tanahjampea, and the Flores Monarch, described only in 1973. There are just a few specimens of the Flores Crow; and the Damar Blue Flycatcher, of Damar, and the Crimson-hooded Honeyeater, of Wetar, have not been recorded for many decades.

Farther west, the Greater Sundas – Sumatra and Java – and adjacent small islands, notably Bali, also have many endemics, more and more of which are at risk as the trees go. One of Bali's most endangered birds is the Bali Starling (75). Various Sumatran and Javan raptors, cuckoos, owls and nightjars have already been mentioned; but a number of smaller birds are causing concern there too. The Black-banded Barbet and White-breasted Babbler are restricted to remnant patches of lowland forest in Java, and Schneider's Pitta to mountain forest in north Sumatra; all are evidently becoming rarer. The Sumatran and Javan Cochoas, large bluish chat-thrushes with pale caps, are also endemic to what is left of these islands'

forests. Rueck's Niltava, a dark blue flycatcher with a metallic blue rump and whitish belly, is known only from a few specimens, some of uncertain origin, but it too is probably endemic to Sumatra.

Christmas Island, an Australian territory 300 km south of Java – not to be confused with the Pacific atoll now known as Kiritimati – holds not only the vulnerable Christmas Imperial Pigeon (*p.134*), but also the Christmas Frigatebird (**76**) and another seabird, Abbott's Booby. The last, which used also to breed near Aldabra (*chapter 5*), is a small, blackish-winged and black-tailed gannet whose world population of under 2000 pairs nests on trees on the central plateau of this one island, and where they are increasingly endangered by phosphate-mining.

Taiwan, off China, has the scarce Yellow Tit restricted to its broadleaved forest. And the Japanese Nansei-shotō (Ryūkū Islands), extending north-east from Taiwan, have some rare endemics apart from the serpent-eagle (*p.133*). For example, the Okinawa Rail, an only recently discovered member of a family that has come to grief on islands the world over (*see p.153 and* **92**), is dependent on indigenous forest in the north of the central island of Okinawa. The same primary forest is shared with the Okinawa Woodpecker, which needs undisturbed old trees (*see also* **7–8**). These two species are endemic to an island where there has been a tendency to fell and replant with aliens; already 'Endangered', only a few dozen pairs of the woodpeckers remain.

But perhaps the most remarkable island of the whole region is Sri Lanka. Despite its closeness to India – the Palk Strait is under 100 km across and, at its narrowest, a mere 30 km – it holds over 20 endemic birds. Some are common and others well protected by long-standing reserves, or at least they were until the recent troubles. Nearly half, however, are rare and dependent on undisturbed forest. Apart from the Sri Lanka Wood Pigeon, Red-faced Malkoha and Green-billed Coucal (*p.134*), others causing concern include the Spot-winged Thrush, Sri Lanka Whistling-thrush (of montane streamsides), Ashy-headed Laughingthrush (a babbler), Sri Lanka Bush-warbler, Legge's Flower-pecker, White-headed Starling, and Sri Lanka Blue Magpie. The last is particularly beautiful, all pale blue with darker shoulders, rufous head and wings, and red bill and legs. For many of these the Peak Wilderness Sanctuary, above 1000 m in the central highlands, is the key area whose forest boundaries must be maintained.

This overview of threatened Indomalayan birds has not mentioned the smaller mainland species. Apart from Gurney's Pitta (77), at least two other pittas are threatened by forest destruction. The Bar-bellied Pitta is endemic to lowland forest in what was Indochina; and the Giant Pitta extends from peninsular Thailand to Sumatra and Borneo, but needs humid lowland forest and is generally very uncommon.

76

CHRISTMAS FRIGATEBIRD

Fregata andrewsi

Frigatebirds are big seabirds with long hooked bills, thin wings often spanning over 2 m, and deep-forked tails. They cannot swim or walk but soar for hours, diving down to snatch flying fish or surfaced squid or offal, or to pursue other seabirds for their prey; they drink in flight and bathe with but momentary contact. Three have wide ranges; a fourth nests only at Ascension. The last of the five species has 1500 unprotected pairs on Christmas Island, south of Java, and no other known colonies. Male frigatebirds are largely blackish with inflatable scarlet throats; this one also has a white belly-patch. Females have white breasts and juveniles white or, as in this species, tawny heads.

77
GURNEY'S PITTA
Pitta gurneyi

Pittas are mostly tropical, brightly coloured, thrush-sized, plump, longish-legged, and very short-tailed. South-east Asia has 22 of the 29 species. Shy, in forest or scrub, they spend much time on the ground, flicking over leaves for snails, worms and insects; only whistles show their presence. Some are mainly brown, but others are green or blue above – or, as here, chestnut with a blue tail. Endemic to peninsular Burma and Thailand, Gurney's was feared extinct through deforestation until rediscovery in 1986. Black head and blue crown, black breast and belly, and slightly barred yellow flanks identify the male; the female has a buff crown and is entirely barred below but for a white throat.

Some chat-thrushes, such as the spectacular Green Cochoa – green with blue crown, wing-patches and tail-base – have wide ranges in upland forest from the Himalayas to south-east China and north Vietnam, but seem rare everywhere; secretive canopy feeders, they may be overlooked, but so much of their forest is going that their distributions are bound to become increasingly fragmented. Other rare thrushes, even less well known, include skulkers of forest undergrowth: for example, in Nepal and Assam, the Rusty-bellied Shortwing, which is short-tailed too; and, from Nepal to the Sino-Vietnamese border, the Blue-fronted Robin, whose male is all blue-black but for blue forehead and shoulder-patches.

Many of the rarer babblers have limited ranges and so are at great risk if their habitats are disturbed: nearly 20 in mainland Indomalaya are currently causing concern. For example, Deignan's Babbler is endemic to bamboo forest on one peak in north-west Thailand; the Short-tailed Scimitar-babbler (with the long decurved bill typical of the scimitars) is restricted to central Vietnam; the Grey-crowned Sibia is found only on one plateau in south Vietnam; and the Marbled Wren-babbler is confined to central peninsular Malaysia and west Sumatra. Half-a-dozen laughingthrushes – so called for the maniacal sounds produced by some species, but nonetheless babblers – are also endemic to small areas of India, south China, Laos or Vietnam; a couple are known only from old specimens.

A number of other families of forest and scrub include similarly rare or little-known species: warblers, flycatchers, tits, flowerpeckers, munias, and weavers. Several nuthatches have restricted ranges in mountains: the White-browed is endemic to one peak in Burma, the Black-masked to southern China, and the Yellow-billed to central Vietnam, all at altitudes over 2500 m. The much larger Beautiful Nuthatch, of the Himalayas to north Vietnam – with brightly blue-streaked crown and mantle – and the even larger Giant Nuthatch, of southernmost China, east Burma and north Thailand – not unlike a European Nuthatch but approaching the size of a Great Spotted Woodpecker – live at lower altitudes down to 1000 m.

The spectacular Silver Oriole – silvery-white with black head and wings, and maroon tail – is endemic to southern China, where much forest has been lost. Two of the secretive crows known as treepies must also be at risk from disappearing habitat in restricted ranges: these are the all dusky Ratchet-tailed Treepie, of east Laos, north Vietnam and Hainan, which has a remarkable 'toothed' tail; and Burma's Hooded Treepie – mainly grey with a black head – whose long tail has a flared tip.

The great majority of threatened birds in south-east Asia are forest species, but two of the rarer parrotbills – distantly related to Bearded Tits – live in reeds, long grass and scrub, as do some scarce warblers. Stoliczka's Bushchat, not unlike a Whinchat, appears now to be far rarer than it was in desert scrub and open grassland from south Afghanistan to north-west India.

Finally, something of a mystery. The White-eyed River Martin is mainly black, glossed blue-green, but differs strikingly from its only close relative, the African River Martin, in its white (not red) eyes, white rump-band, and greatly elongated central tail-shafts with thin racket-tips. The species was unknown until 1968, when it was first caught by bird-trappers in a winter roost at a reservoir in central Thailand. In the next few years over 100 were taken for the local markets: inevitably, all soon died in captivity. Now protected from capture or hunting in Thailand, few have been seen since the late 1970s. Where they breed is unknown – perhaps north Thailand or south China – but numbers must be small and the species possibly on the verge of extinction. Trapping and reed-harvesting at that reservoir have caused marked declines among other swallows, too, illustrating once again the serious impact of the birdcatchers and the cagebird trade.

New Guinea, Australia, New Zealand and related islands

In faunistic terms Australasia (Austral, or 'south [of]', Asia) covers not only Australia and New Zealand, together with their close islands, but also New Guinea and many smaller archipelagos. The region takes in the Indonesian islands west to at least the Moluccas and Tanimbar. East of New Guinea, it includes the rest of Melanesia through the Solomons to Vanuatu and New Caledonia, all extensions of the New Guinea folds; but the smaller and more isolated Pacific islands of Micronesia and tropical Polynesia are here treated separately (*chapter 8*). Thus, the region includes a continent (Australia), a few sizeable islands (such as New Guinea, Tasmania, and the two of New Zealand) and thousands of smaller to tiny islands of mainly continental origin.

The old boundary between the Australasian and Indomalayan regions, known as Wallace's Line, ran between Borneo and Sulawesi and between Bali and Lombok; the differences between the avifaunas of the latter two islands only 30 km apart in the Sunda chain are remarkably sharp (*chapter 6*), and there are also many distinctions between Borneo and Sulawesi. Yet the whole of the geographical area known as Wallacea, from Wallace's Line east to include the Moluccas, Seram and all the Lesser Sundas, is something of a transitional zone between the two regions.

Australia is of course the smallest of the continents; and, with a total land area of just under 9 million square km, the Australasian is the smallest of the main zoogeographical regions (excluding the Malagasy and Pacific island groupings). It spans over 50 degrees of latitude southwards from just north of the equator, and more than two-fifths of the landmass lies within

the tropics. The rest is temperate, but even in the south of New Zealand mean temperatures in July and January differ by only about 9°C, in the range 5–14°C. Tropical lowland New Guinea has temperatures in the range 22–34°C.

Since winter mean temperatures in southern New Zealand and Tasmania are as high as 5°C and 7°C, migration from the southern parts of the region in the austral winter, although it does occur, is mostly short-distance or nomadic, and often does not include the whole population of any species. No essentially Australasian landbirds reach the Palearctic. And few Palearctic landbirds reach Australasia with any regularity in the northern winter: just one or two accipiters in Indonesia, the Oriental Cuckoo, at least two swifts,

78

ORANGE-BELLIED PARROT
Neophema chrysogaster

More than a third of the world's 350 parrots live in Australasia; most are endemic. New Guinea and nearby islands hold over 60, and Australia itself over 50. Many are common, if local, but eight in Australia are causing concern. One is the rare Orange-bellied Parrot that breeds in heathland copses in western Tasmania, and winters on saltmarshes and dunes on the adjacent south coast of Australia. Its range was always limited, and it appears to have decreased after development of large parts of its wintering grounds. Entirely rich green but for a yellower face, orange-centred yellow belly, and violet-blue strips on forehead and wings, this grass parakeet is not much bigger than a Budgerigar.

79

FRECKLED DUCK
Stictonetta naevosa

*This strange and rather dull-looking duck, which has
no really close relatives, often looks all dark, even
though speckled white or buff. Males are blacker,
females browner; brown-mottled white wing-linings
show in flight. The large head has a rear peak, and
the flattened grey bill a high base that is variably
orange-red on males. Endemic to well-vegetated lakes
and swamps in south-east and far south-west
Australia, these ducks wander more widely at times
of drought. There are probably still several thousands
but, despite legal protection, they are at risk from
excessive shooting – sometimes of hundreds in a
single area – as well as from drought, drainage and,
in some parts, water-sports.*

the Barn Swallow, four wagtails, and the Great Reed-warbler. On the other hand, over 20 Palearctic waders regularly spend the northern winter in Australia, some in large numbers; another 20 occur as vagrants.

Australia is a low-lying continent, mostly below 1000 m and nowhere much over 2000 m. The highest areas and most rugged scenery are in the east, with lesser uplands in the west and centre. Rainfall is highest in the north and east, rather less in the south-west, and lowest in the west and the vast empty spaces of the interior. In the interior, stony deserts, fixed dunes, hummock grassland, and low shrubland with saltbush give way in concentric circles to semi-arid open shrublands, the scrub or mallee of the south, the grasslands of the river floodplains and the north, the heaths of the south and east, the acacia woodlands, and the coastal eucalyptus forests. Australia is usually divided into three subregions: the tropical north, the temperate south, and the arid interior.

Inland waters, including the rivers in dry regions, are unreliable and not even seasonal, because of uncertain rainfall and high evaporation. The largest lakes, Eyre and Torrens, are only a few thousand square km if filled, and the water there is saline. The Murray–Darling river complex has a drainage basin approaching one million square km. The deepest freshwater lakes are in the uplands, the most extensive in Tasmania; many others, even in areas of higher rainfall, dry out annually or periodically. The coasts include mangroves, saltmarshes, dunes and cliffs.

In contrast, temperate New Zealand and tropical New Guinea have high mountains and rich vegetation. Of New Zealand's two main islands, North rises to almost 2800 m, while South's Mount Cook stands at nearly 3800 m. Much of New Zealand's dense evergreen forest of southern beeches and yew-pines, tangled with palms and ferns, was destroyed in the first century of European settlement – long before the tropical rainforests elsewhere were threatened – to be replaced by grasslands for sheep.

New Guinea has coastal mountains and a central backbone with several peaks of well over 4000 m with permanent snow and, highest of them all, Puntjak Jaya at just over 5000 m. Still extensive rainforests – now the third largest after those in Brazil and Zaïre – are succeeded by pines and palms at higher levels to a tree limit at around 3000 m. The western half of New Guinea, Irian Jaya, is part of Indonesia; the eastern half is part of Papua New Guinea, which includes the Bismarck Archipelago, New Britain, and Bougainville.

The southern hills and lowlands of New Guinea are, in many ways, an extension of northern Australia; the two have been joined several times in geological history, most recently about 10,000 years ago. Consequently, a number of the characteristic groups of vertebrates are shared, including the marsupial carnivores, bandicoots, possums and kangaroos, as well as the monotreme anteaters. Thus, it is usual to look at New Guinea (with its adjacent islands), Australia and Tasmania together as the Australo-Papuan area. That has been extended here to include the Solomons and thence down to Vanuatu and New Caledonia.

New Zealand has marked differences and its own peculiarities, not least the fact that some of its commonest birds are among the 30 or so species that the early settlers introduced; in fact, it is a corner of the Polynesian triangle and some of its affinities are with the tropical islands to the north (*chapter 8*).

Indigenous birds

Australia, with Tasmania, has some 580 breeding birds; another 170 occur as migrants or vagrants. This may not seem a large number for a continent of its size, but expressed as 75 indigenous species per million square km it compares favourably with Africa and puts the northern continents completely in the shade.

Although less than one-eighth the size, New Guinea has some 620 breeding species. About half of these are shared with Australia; the total for the two main landmasses of the Australo-Papuan area is just over 900. With New Zealand and all the smaller islands of the region, the number of indigenous breeding birds rises to some 1385. In total, that is less than any of the other tropical and southern continental regions, but at around 155 species per million square km it comes third only behind the Indomalayan and Neotropical.

The Australasian region as a whole has over 80 indigenous families of birds. Nearly three-quarters are cosmopolitan groups of larger birds of sea, fresh water or land (*p.15*), or at least widely distributed in the tropics or eastern Asia. More southerly marine families well represented include penguins, albatrosses and diving-petrels. Other water-associated groups are grebes, pelicans, darters, cormorants, herons, ibises and spoonbills, ducks, rails, cranes, oystercatchers, stilts and avocets, plovers, sandpipers, pratincoles, skuas, gulls, and terns.

Among landbirds, nearly half the world's button-quails are found in this region, which also has more than its share of pigeons, parrots, barn-owls and kingfishers. Well represented, too, are hawks and eagles, falcons, cuckoos, owls, nightjars, and swifts.

On the other hand, there are rather few cosmopolitan families among the passerines. Those belonging to widely distributed groups in world terms include four swallows, a dozen thrushes and chats, some 20 Old World warblers, only six typical flycatchers, a dozen starlings, seven orioles, and eleven crows, but little else. For example, there is just one lark (a second has been introduced) and, similarly, two pipits; wagtails occur only as migrants.

Of common tropical Afro-Asian families, Australasia has nearly 30 cuckoo-shrikes, some three dozen white-eyes, and a similar number of grassfinches and mannikins, but only five babblers, two sunbirds and five drongos. Otherwise mainly Indomalayan families are represented by six pittas, over two dozen fantails and nearly twice as many monarch-flycatchers, some 40 whistlers, and 17 flowerpeckers.

About 20 families (and over 1150 species) are endemic to the Australasian region, while three or four more families are almost or largely restricted to it, to the point of being essentially Australasian – higher numbers than in any other region except the Neotropical. Sixteen endemic families of the Australo-Papuan area are the emus, cassowaries, plains-wanderers, owlet-nightjars, lyrebirds, scrub-birds, fairy-wrens, sittellas, Australian treecreepers, pardalotes, Australian chats, bowerbirds, birds-of-paradise, mudnesters, magpie-larks, and butcherbirds and currawongs. New Zealand, as shown later, adds another three and New Caledonia a further one.

Of the dozen megapodes, the six brush-turkeys and the Malleefowl are confined to Australasia, but the outlying scrubfowls extend as far as the Nicobars, Philippines and Polynesia, and the Maleo lives in Sulawesi (*see* 68). Almost exclusive to this region, too, are the 19 log-runners, quail-thrushes and rail-babblers, only one of which extends to Malaysia; and the 70-odd thornbills and flyeaters, only two of which are otherwise found in south-east Asia and the Lesser Sundas. Eight of the ten wood-swallows are in Australasia, though some extend to the Indomalayan and Pacific regions. Most of the large family of some 170 honeyeaters are in the Australasian (over 150) and Pacific regions, including 68 in Australia itself; otherwise there are just a dozen on Indonesian islands (Indomalayan region) and one on the Ogasawara-shotō (Palearctic).

80

NOISY SCRUB-BIRD

Atrichornis clamosus

Related to the ornate and much larger lyrebirds, the two Australian scrub-birds are usually placed in their own family. The Noisy lives in dense scrub on one headland in the far south-west, the smaller Rufous in montane forest tangles in the east. They are small-bodied with stubby wings and longish graduated tails fanned in display. Heard more than seen, they fly little, but run mouse-like with tails cocked. Both are rare. The Noisy was feared extinct for 70 years to 1961; now, with conservation, there are over 200. Finely barred above, it has a white throat, the male's divided by a black triangle above the chest, and a rich buff vent. The loud penetrating song seems ventriloquial.

81
EYREAN GRASSWREN
Amytornis goyderi

In the same Australian family as the colourful fairy-wrens, the eight grasswrens are shy, long-tailed, terrestrial birds that are very hard to see in dense cover and prefer running to flying. Several with small ranges are at risk from drought, fire or development. Thus, the Eyrean Grasswren – named after Eyre Creek – was hardly known until numbers were found in desert canegrass in 1976; the next year drought left only a few survivors. Some 15 cm long, rusty streaked with white above and whitish-grey below with rufous flanks, the Eyrean has a thicker bill than the others and is more of a seed-eater. Its main call is a faint two-note whistle, but some grasswrens have short melodious songs.

What is scarce or missing in the way of Asiatic and, especially, Indomalayan families is revealing. There are one or two each of storks, cranes, bustards, jacanas, thick-knees, painted-snipes, pratincoles, frog-mouths, bee-eaters and rollers, but no pheasants, trogons, barbets or woodpeckers. The only indigenous gamebirds are half-a-dozen quails. Hornbills, significant features of the Afrotropical and Indomalayan regions, are almost absent: one species reaches New Guinea and the Solomons. Songbird families missing include broadbills, titmice, fairy-bluebirds, sparrows (only introduced), true finches, and buntings, while the only indigenous bulbul extends no farther to the east than the Moluccas.

Endemic families of New Zealand are the kiwis (three), New Zealand wrens (four, two extinct) and New Zealand wattlebirds (three, one extinct). Other endemic species include four penguins, a grebe, an albatross, six petrels and three shearwaters, seven cormorants, four ducks, one falcon, three rails and gallinules, two oystercatchers, one stilt, four plovers, two snipes, one gull, two terns, one pigeon, six parrots, two cuckoos, one owl, three flycatchers, one Old World warbler, five flyeaters and other Australasian warblers, and three honeyeaters – bringing the total to 72. It should be added that, although breeding only in New Zealand, most of the seabirds wander elsewhere, sometimes quite widely, at other seasons, while the two cuckoos spread over the Solomon Islands and a vast area of Polynesia.

Although New Zealand has a bird list of some 300 species, less than one-sixth are indigenous landbirds, but 37 of those are endemic. In Britain, by way of contrast, there are twice as many indigenous landbirds, but only one is endemic.

Introductions

Man's introductions of animals into countries where they do not belong has had profound effects on indigenous species. Many introductions are unintentional – such as shipborne rats, feral cats, or escaped cagebirds establishing feral populations – but others have been deliberate. Among birds, the latter have often included waterfowl as lake ornaments;

gamebirds to shoot at for sport or food; specialist feeders and hunters intended to 'control' a variety of pests from insects to rats; and familiar European species taken along by homesick early colonists.

House Sparrows, once largely confined to Europe, have been transported and spread over many parts of the world. To a lesser extent, Common Starlings are now present in five continents. Common Pheasants, primarily Asiatic in origin, cover considerable areas of Europe and North America. The varied descendants of Rock Pigeons, brought in soon after European colonisation, are even more ubiquitous.

But these are strongly competitive and successful birds that are readily able to exploit niches associated with Man. Most introduced birds have some difficulty in becoming established, except on small islands where natural competitors are fewer and less able to resist. In general, introductions of birds to continents and to large islands have usually had only relatively local significance for the indigenous populations.

In Australia, releases of nearly 100 species have resulted in feral or semi-feral populations of over 30; about a third of each of these figures, however, relates

82
SALMON-CRESTED COCKATOO
Cacatua moluccensis

Many of the 19 cockatoos live in Australia; the rest in New Guinea and other islands from the Philippines to the Solomons. These mostly large parrots with mobile crests are white or black, or pink or grey, with touches of red and yellow; bare eye-patches give a knowing look. The Salmon-crested, of the south Moluccas, is all pale salmon-pink but for darker undersides to the curved crest, flight-feathers and tail-base; these latter show in flight, as fast beats are interspersed with short glides. All cockatoos eat seeds and nuts. This one uses its short deep bill to 'gnaw' young coconuts, so some are shot as pests. But the real cause of its decline is massive exploitation for the cagebird trade.

to translocated Australian species (such as Emus, Brush-turkeys, Common Bronzewings and Crested Pigeons to Kangaroo Island, Superb Lyrebirds to Tasmania, Sulphur-crested Cockatoos, other parrots and Red-browed Waxbills to Western Australia, and Laughing Kookaburras to all three areas).

Among the larger exotic introductions are Ostriches in South Australia; Mute Swans and Mallards in the south and east; various gamebirds, including California Quails, Common Pheasants, Indian Peafowls, Helmeted Guineafowls and Common Turkeys, mainly on offshore islands; and Spotted Doves in the south and east. Many of the songbirds are of European origin, but, apart from House Sparrows and Common Starlings which are rather widespread in the east, most are only in the south-east and often very local. These include Sky Larks, Blackbirds, Song Thrushes, Goldfinches, Greenfinches, and Tree Sparrows.

House Crows, ship-assisted from India and southeast Asia to ports in southern Australia since the 1920s, have fortunately never established themselves as they have around other parts of the Indian Ocean (*pp.82, 105*). Among other Asiatic species, both Nutmeg Mannikins and Common Mynahs are now well established in several eastern areas of Australia (where the mynahs cause damage to fruit crops, especially figs) and Red-whiskered Bulbuls are found more locally in the south-east. Two African birds, the White-winged Whydah and Red Bishop, also have small feral populations in the south-east.

For most artificially introduced birds in Australia, therefore, 'local' and 'scarce' are the operative words. In New Zealand, however, several of the 13 European songbirds that were brought in from the 1860s onwards have become the dominant landbirds of the country. This is a unique example of larger islands being taken over in this way and it happened because everything was in the introduced birds' favour. European colonists were replacing the natural forest with farmland and introduced crops, providing ideal habitats and food supply for European birds in a comparable climate; the indigenous species were swamped before they had a chance to adapt.

Thus, apart from Feral Pigeons, Starlings and House Sparrows, as well as Mallards and Common Pheasants, some of the most numerous birds in New Zealand now are Sky Larks, Song Thrushes, Blackbirds, Dunnocks, Greenfinches, Goldfinches, Redpolls, Chaffinches and Yellowhammers. Several of these, having become abundant in New Zealand itself, have spread to distant satellite islands, such as the Auckland and Campbell Islands, and even Macquarie more than 1000 km away to the south-west (*chapter 9*). Others have been introduced separately to such island groups as Chatham, Lord Howe, Norfolk and Kermadec.

In fact, nearly 130 exotic species have at one time or another been released in New Zealand – a total second only to Hawaii (*see chapter 8*) – and over 30 of those have become established. Other less successful or more locally distributed western Palearctic birds there include Grey Partridges, Chukars, Little Owls, Rooks and Cirl Buntings.

From North America, there are also Canada Geese and California Quails; from Asia, Spotted Doves and, abundantly, Common Mynahs; from Australia, Black Swans, Brown Quails, two of the rosellas, Sulphur-crested Cockatoos, Laughing Kookaburras and Australian Magpies; and, from domesticated stock, Helmeted Guineafowls, Common Turkeys and Barbary Doves. Populations of American Bobwhite Quails and Asiatic Red-vented Bulbuls, however, became as unsuccessful as many introductions in other parts of the world: the former simply died out after about 60 years, and the bulbuls were exterminated. Failed attempts at introductions have included European plovers and a sandgrouse. Grey-backed White-eyes (Silver-eyes) colonised themselves by a large-scale immigration from Australia in the late 1850s.

As in Australia, a number of New Zealand birds have also been translocated, often moved to small islands offshore, for conservation and other purposes. For example, Brown Kiwis have been established on Kapiti and Little Barrier Islands; Wekas, flightless rails, have been reintroduced to quite a number of places, and also moved as far south as Macquarie (*chapter 9*); and Saddlebacks have been introduced to various islands close to the main ones.

Extinctions

The European colonisation of Australia and New Zealand in the seventeenth century, and earlier Polynesian settlement of New Zealand, resulted in the extinction of several large flightless ratites. While the Emu survived in mainland Australia to become the national bird, the dwarf forms of Tasmania, King Island and Kangaroo Island, between half and three-quarters the size, were wiped out by the early 1800s.

The Polynesians, wherever they went in the Pacific, were potentially almost as damaging as the Europeans that followed them: they introduced rats, dogs and other mammals, they burnt and cut forest, and they hunted. The moas of New Zealand included the largest recorded birds, but most of the dozen to 20 or more species were exterminated before or, in two cases, probably during the seventeenth century. All are

83
RIBBON-TAILED ASTRAPIA
Astrapia mayeri

Most of the 42 birds-of-paradise, including all five astrapias, live in New Guinea's montane forests, others in Australia and the Moluccas; 11 with small ranges seem at risk from deforestation and hunting. Many have the look of crows or starlings, though bill-shape may be short and stout (fruit-eaters) to thin and curved (insect-eaters). Some males have strange plumages: reds, oranges, yellows, greens or blues, and long, soft or peculiarly shaped plumes that may bring the total length to a metre. Astrapias, here female and male, are far from being the most striking. All have complicated displays; some even hang upside down. Many are polygamous: such males display communally.

84
VICTORIA CROWNED PIGEON
Goura victoria

The three species of crowned pigeons, all endemic to New Guinea, are confined to forests; unlike most pigeons, they lay only one egg. They are characterised by their huge, laterally flattened and lacy-looking crests several times the size of the head. This spectacular feathering has long attracted hunters. The Victoria and Maroon-breasted Crowned Pigeons are both likely to be at some risk, though there is still much suitable habitat; the Blue Crowned Pigeon is probably more numerous. The ground-nesting Solomon Islands Crowned Pigeon, better known as Meek's Pigeon, is almost certainly extinct: not recorded since the early 1900s, it was very different, with a far less spectacular crest.

known only from bones, fossils, feathers and eggs, but one of the smallest, confined to South Island, may have survived until at least 1785 and just possibly into the nineteenth century.

Luckily the kiwis did not share the moas' fate, perhaps partly because of their secretiveness and nocturnal habits, but another terrestrial (though not flightless) species that did was the New Zealand Quail in about 1875. The New Zealand Little Bittern lasted until about 1900, and the Auckland Islands Merganser until at least 1905.

Most notable, however, of the extinct New Zealand birds that survived into the twentieth century was the Huia, exterminated by 1907. A wattlebird related to the endangered Kokako and the threatened Saddleback (*p.163*), it was remarkable for the sexual differences in the bill, the male's short and thick, the female's long and downcurved: both hunted grubs in decayed wood, but the male chiselled and the female probed.

New Zealand has evidently lost a number of other landbirds. The Laughing Owl has not been certainly recorded since 1914, despite occasional claims through to the 1980s. There used to be three subspecies of the

Bush-wren, but the North Island race apparently survived only to the 1950s, the Stewart Island form to the 1970s, and the South Island race to the 1980s; rats and cats have often been the problem. The Piopio, or New Zealand 'Thrush', one of the family of whistlers or 'thickheads', may actually have been lost in the early part of the century, though sightings were reported in 1955 and possibly 1963. Any of these three species could still exist, though it is thought unlikely.

In contrast to New Zealand, Australia's birds have got away with things comparatively lightly. Apart from the dwarf emus, the only Australian bird extinct since 1600 – and even that is not absolutely certain – is south-east Queensland's Paradise Parrot.

All the other Australasian extinctions since 1600 have been on the smaller islands. Among the worst sufferers was the Chatham archipelago, 800 km east of New Zealand. The Chatham Swan went in the seventeenth century, and the Chatham Banded Rail in about 1840; another rail, the Modest Rail of Pitt and Mangare, two small islands of the same group, lasted until about 1900. Several more endemic birds there are now at risk (*pp.161–2*).

KAGU

Rhynochetos jubatus

*About 60 cm long, this odd whitish-grey bird with
red-orange bill and legs is the sole species in its
family. It is flightless but can glide downhill on
rounded wings – which then show bars of white,
black and rufous – and it runs fast. It lives socially
and eats earthworms; loud melodious notes at first
light, often from pairs in duet, contrast with
otherwise harsh calls. Once widespread on New
Caledonia – 1200 km east of Australia – it was hunted
for its loose crest-plumes (which it raises in threat),
suffered from introduced dogs, cats, rats and pigs,
and lost out to logging, burning and opencast mining:
probably only a few hundreds remain in the least
accessible mountain forests.*

Rails and gallinules are often represented on islands, and almost as often endangered by Man's chopping, burning, draining, hunting and, not least, introductions. The so-called White Swamphen of Lord Howe Island, 600 km east of Australia, was wiped out by 1834; and there may have been a related species on Norfolk Island, nearly 1000 km farther north-east. Yet another rail, the Wood Rail of New Caledonia, has not been recorded since 1904, but might conceivably still exist on that relatively unworked island that is almost the size of Wales.

It was these same three islands that held most of the other extinctions. The New Caledonian Lorikeet, a small parrot, has not definitely been recorded since 1860 (but may have been seen in 1970) and the New Caledonian Owlet-frogmouth not since 1880; either could still survive. The Lord Howe White-eye and the Norfolk Island Starling, on the other hand, were certainly lost in the 1920s. The latter lived on both Norfolk and nearby Philip Islands, as did the Norfolk Island Parrot which was related to the Kaka of New Zealand and exterminated by 1851. The Solomon Islands Crowned Pigeon, quite different from the now

PENGUIN PROBLEMS,
AND THE YELLOW-EYED PENGUIN
Megadyptes antipodes

Penguins tend to be thought of as confined to Antarctica, where huge numbers breed. But several species nest north to latitudes that are the southern hemisphere equivalents of the United States and Mediterranean; indeed, South America's Galapagos and Humboldt Penguins are actually tropical. All are flightless and adapted for life in the sea: their wings have become narrow flippers for swimming, and their short legs, set far back, are more suited to steering than walking; wet and cold are combated by a dense pile of specialised feathering and a thick layer of insulating fat.

Penguins that nest on temperate and tropical mainlands and inshore islands – South America's Humboldt and Magellanic, South Africa's Jackass, and New Zealand's Yellow-eyed – are all causing concern. They have long suffered any or all of such interferences as human disturbance, land clearance and development, the cropping of eggs, the collection of guano, and the attentions of introduced predators. Though all now enjoy legal protection in a climate of greater ecological awareness – or appreciation of the financial advantages of wildlife tourism – they still have to face continuing development, pollution and, not least, human overharvesting of their foods: fish, squids and krill.

Three-quarters of the 16–18 penguin species have occurred in southern Australasia, notably in the waters of New Zealand and its satellite islands, to which four or five are indeed restricted. Most threatened of these, and one of the world's rarest, is the Yellow-eyed. Except for the largest and the smallest species, which are paler, adult penguins in general are blue-black to blackish-grey above and white below, with black, grey, orange or, commonly, pinkish feet; they differ most in colours and patterns of heads and bills. A medium-sized species about 70 cm long, the Yellow-eyed has a cap of black-shafted yellow feathers, giving its head a golden tinge, bordered by a clear yellow band encircling the rear crown from behind its red-brown bill and cold yellow eyes.

Apart from populations on the sub-antarctic Campbell and Auckland Islands several hundred kilometres to the south of New Zealand, Yellow-eyed Penguins nest only on Stewart Island and the southern and eastern shores of South Island. Adults are generally sedentary, at sea by day and on shore at night, but the grey-eyed juveniles – less distinctive without the yellowish cap, and with the yellow band restricted to the sides of the head – tend to disperse from the breeding areas.

Many penguins nest in huge rookeries, but this one usually breeds singly or in small loose groups. Nests are in coastal scrub and forest, in the shelter of bushes, logs, rocks or cliffs. They may be half a kilometre inland, and involve the crossing of soft sand, rough ground or small cliffs several times a day with food for the chicks. Like other inshore penguins of temperate regions, this is mainly a fish-eater.

Males are in excess on South Island and, although the Yellow-eyed can breed when two years old, some may have to wait up to ten years before they can mate. Two-year-old females produce only one egg, often infertile. Older birds usually lay two, with a greater chance of hatching. Fresh egg to sea-going juvenile takes five or six months, during which a lot can go wrong.

Land clearance for human settlement has destroyed much of this penguin's habitat, especially on South Island, and cats, rats, ferrets and other introduced predators have taken a steady toll. Numbers are declining on the mainland, very possibly also on Stewart Island and the two sub-antarctic archipelagos. The outlook is poor, the species may not be safe anywhere, and a number of smaller breeding areas have already been deserted. Fortunately, Yellow-eyed Penguins seem able to tolerate some disturbance, and continue to use traditional sites if not actually interfered with. Much will depend on protection, management and, not least, education.

Of the others endemic to the New Zealand area, Fiordland Penguins, with broad yellow eyebrows, are restricted to South and Stewart Islands. The related Snares and Erect-crested, which nest only on archipelagos farther south, also have lateral yellow crests, bushy at the rear on one, upright and brush-like on the other. South Island's Banks Peninsula holds the small White-flippered – all blue-grey above – but that is probably just a race of Australasia's Little Penguin.

The Erect-crested still breeds in vast rookeries on the Bounty and Antipodes Islands, but overfishing is already a problem in southern waters and, if there is development of these islands or, appalling thought, of Antarctica itself, the losses could be enormous.

threatened crowned pigeons of New Guinea (*see* **84**), has not been recorded since 1904, but might just survive on Choiseul.

A tale to conclude the saga of extinctions concerns the Stephens Island Wren, a relative of the New Zealand Bush-wren, which was restricted to that one small island in the Cook Strait. Just discovered in 1894, the species was only ever seen alive by the lighthouse-keeper, who said it ran like a mouse and did not fly; unfortunately, the whole population was killed off that very year by the lighthouse cat, thus illustrating at one fell pounce the vulnerability of island birds to introduced mammals.

Threatened birds

If the illustrations with this chapter seem to favour New Zealand, it is because that country and its associated islands hold some of the world's most seriously threatened birds: no fewer than 12 are classed as 'Endangered'. In contrast – apart from two more on Lord Howe and Norfolk Islands – the 1988 list shows Australia with only two species 'Endangered'; moreover, one of those is probably extinct and the

other's numbers are now above the critical level. Indeed, relatively few Australian birds are, as species, even causing particular concern.

Seven of those are parrots, or eight if the almost certainly extinct Paradise Parrot still exists. This beautiful bird – the male brown and turquoise with red forehead, shoulders and belly – is, or was, closely related to the Golden-shouldered Parrot of north Queensland and the Hooded Parrot of the Northern Territory. These latter two, sometimes treated as races of one species, are also rare and threatened. Both are found in savannah and eucalyptus woodlands, among the termite mounds in which they nest. Droughts, bush fires and, not least, illegal trapping for the cagebird trade appear to be the main threats.

Two more Australian parrots are apparently rare, but little known because they live in the vast arid shrublands of the interior. One is the nomadic Alexandra's Parrot, long-tailed, pale olive and greyish with blue crown, pink throat, yellow-green shoulders and violet rump. The other is the shy, mysterious and short-tailed Night Parrot; hard to find by day, it lives on the ground and, when flushed, flies only a short

87

PARKINSON'S BLACK PETREL
Procellaria parkinsoni

Of over 70 petrels and shearwaters, a third – including eight in Australasia – are already at risk, in general from human disturbance or, worse, introduced predators on their nest islands. Breeding in the austral summer and then wandering the tropical Pacific, Parkinson's Petrel can muster 1000 pairs at most, all on Little and Great Barrier Islands, New Zealand, where feral cats have long been a problem. The larger but otherwise almost identical Westland Black Petrel – which, in contrast, breeds in the winter – also has a limited nesting area, in forested hills in one part of South Island, but now numbers some thousands, possibly because of an increase in commercial fish offal.

distance before dropping and running for cover. It bears some resemblance to the much larger Kakapo of New Zealand (*see* **91**) with its hidden bill and slightly owl-like head. The same applies to the rather similar but greener and longer-tailed Ground Parrot of coastal south-eastern Australia, Tasmania and one area of Western Australia; also crepuscular and nocturnal, it lives in heath and sedge and, if the Night Parrot be likened to a quail in its short flight, this one more resembles a snipe as it shoots up and away before dropping into thick cover. It is certainly decreasing and has disappeared from some of its range; the main problems appear to be development and disturbance of one sort or another in its coastal habitats.

The last two threatened Australian parrots are the Orange-bellied (**78**) and the closely related and similar-sized but even more colourful Scarlet-chested, which differs mainly in its blue face, scarlet breast and all-yellow belly. The latter has a wider range in Western and South Australia and lives in mulga (acacia) and mallee (dwarf eucalyptus), but is generally uncommon. Although popular as cagebirds, these two parrots are fortunately not difficult to breed in captivity.

Mention of mallee brings us to the Malleefowl, one of the scrubfowls and brush-turkeys that form the megapode family (*see also* **68**). All this group lay eggs in pits in beaches or sandy soil, or in mounds of vegetable matter often several metres across, in which incubation is then by solar or volcanic heat or fermentation. Apart from such nest-parasites as certain cuckoos, cowbirds, honeyguides and whydahs, megapodes are the only birds that show no parental care whatsoever.

Malleefowls spend months on constructing their mounds, first digging a hole over a metre deep and up to 5 m across, then filling it with plant material which, after it has been dampened by rain, is covered with sand or soil to ferment. Up to 35 eggs are laid in this compost heap, each beginning to incubate straight away. The adults maintain a constant temperature by opening and reclosing the mound to allow the heat

88

CHATHAM BLACK ROBIN
Petroica traversi

The Chathams, 800 km east of New Zealand, illustrate Man's disastrous influence on island wildlife, and modern attempts to undo the damage. Three endemic birds are extinct, four more 'Endangered'. Saving the Black Robin is a Conservation Department project. Cats and other introductions almost wiped out these dusky little birds; by 1976 just seven remained, on Little Mangere, and their scrub forest was deteriorating. Five were taken to nearby Mangere, where native trees had been planted and predators removed. There still being only 11 by 1983, the first clutches laid were moved to nests of the Chatham Tomtit (another 'robin') on Rangatira. By 1990 the total was 116.

89
SHORE PLOVER
Thinornis novaeseelandiae

This smallish plover has a white band around its crown and, below that, a black or dark brown face extending back as a collar; the short legs and base of the longish bill are orange. Once widespread, if uncommon, along New Zealand's coasts, it went in the early decades of European colonisation. Now it is confined to Rangatira in the Chatham group, where there are 150–250: they survive only because the island is free of the introduced cats and rats that exterminated these tame birds on the other Chathams. They live mainly around the shore, but also inland on barren ground with scattered trees. Unlike most plovers, they nest in tunnels of thick vegetation or stones, even in old petrel burrows.

to escape and, later, increasing or decreasing the sand cover to allow constant penetration by the sun. The chicks dig themselves out, the first leaving before the later eggs are laid, and are immediately independent, being able to fly within 24 hours. The eggs are frequently taken by local people, monitor lizards, pigs, foxes and so on. Although the Malleefowl has a wide range from Western Australia to New South Wales, it is decreasing with the clearance of its habitat and has already disappeared from some areas.

Other larger Australian birds thought to be at some risk include the Freckled Duck (**79**); two raptors, the rare and secretive Red Hawk of northern coastal woodlands and the Grey Falcon of the arid zone; the Black-breasted Buttonquail; the curious Plains-wanderer, something like an erect buttonquail with a

thin bill but now considered an aberrant grassland wader; the small but striking Hooded Plover; and the Pacific Gull with its massive bill. The Red Hawk – usually called the Red Goshawk, though it is not related to the true goshawks – is notable for its rufous colour and massive feet; the female is the size of a small eagle.

Though some are simply uncommon to rare, the main problems for many of these species are habitat destruction, development, and disturbance. The same applies to the small Australian birds at risk. These include the two scrub-birds (80); the Eyrean Grasswren (81) and four other Australasian wrens; the two bristlebirds; and the Regent Honeyeater. Of these, only the Noisy Scrub-bird was officially classed as 'Endangered' and it has, with protection, built up its numbers so well that it cannot now be regarded as anything more than 'Rare'. In eastern Tasmania, the Forty-spotted Pardalote, a small Australasian warbler, may also be threatened by habitat destruction.

Two other Australian passerines have rather different problems. A second honeyeater, the Black-eared Miner, does suffer from clearance of mallee scrub, but is more seriously threatened by genetic swamping: it is interbreeding in its small south-eastern range with the rather similar and very widespread Yellow-throated Miner. The Gouldian Finch – boldly painted in green, lilac, yellow and blue, with a black, red or ochre face – is an elegant and famous little bird of northern parts of Australia: it is declining, in at least parts of its range, from a parasite infection.

Lord Howe and Norfolk, two Australian Islands well to the east, have already been mentioned. The former is the home of the Lord Howe Woodhen, a once numerous flightless rail that had been reduced to a handful of pairs by the late 1970s, particularly through the predations of introduced cats, rats and Australian Masked Owls. Steps were taken to reduce these predators, and Woodhens were bred in captivity. The population was thus raised to 200 by 1984, then fell back to a tenth of that figure. The species is classed as 'Endangered', as is the White-breasted White-eye of Norfolk Island, reduced by the early 1980s to less than 50; it has suffered from loss of forest habitat and probably from competition with the related and highly successful Silver-eye, which in the past 200 years has spread from Australia to colonise the south-west Pacific as far as New Zealand and Fiji. Feral cats may also have played a part in the white-eye's decline.

Thus, some 30 birds are listed as likely to be at risk in Australia and Tasmania, but in New Guinea and its associated islands, together with the Moluccas to the west, the Solomons to the east and south to Vanuatu and New Caledonia, the total is three times as high.

The Indonesian Moluccas, here taken as the limit of the Australasian region, hold several endemic species, some limited to a single island. These include the Moluccan Scrubfowl, the rare and interestingly named Invisible Rail, the Obi Woodcock, the Lesser Masked Owl, and half-a-dozen parrots seriously threatened by the cagebird trade. Among the last are two cockatoos: the White Cockatoo on Halmahera and Obi, and the Salmon-crested (82) on Seram. Rare songbirds which are thought to be at risk on these islands and also on Tanimbar, Kai and Aru to the south include two thrushes, a flycatcher, a monarch, a fantail, two white-eyes, and two friarbirds (honeyeaters).

Mainland New Guinea has around 20 birds that are causing concern, though the status of some is insufficiently known and probably none is 'Endangered'. Half are birds-of-paradise, like the Ribbon-tailed Astrapia (83). The rest include an eagle, two of the three crowned pigeons (84), two parrots, a warbler, a whistler, three honeyeaters and a bowerbird. Like the Great Philippine Eagle (see 72), the New Guinea Eagle is a large eagle of the harpy group: short-winged and long-tailed, it is a forest bird whose range extends high into the mountains; the total numbers probably do not exceed a thousand or two, but it is threatened only by deforestation.

The same applies to several others of these New Guinea species, most of which (including the birds-of-paradise) have limited ranges in forest areas, though the Fly River Grass-warbler and Brass's Friarbird are swampland species, both with very restricted ranges.

The remarkable Pesquet's Parrot, which shares with the Vulturine Parrot of the Amazon the distinction of a bare head covered with bristles, is a mountain-forest bird that is also the only parrot to feed entirely on soft fruit, not seeds or nuts; its feathers are used for native head-dresses, but again deforestation will be the real danger. Similarly, for example, the Adelbert Bowerbird is confined to a relatively small area of mountain forest in the coastal Adelbert Range; like related species, it builds a decorated 'bower' of vegetation to attract the rather drab females.

The satellite islands of New Guinea hold a number of endemic birds. Bruijn's Brush-turkey, for example, ia a mound-building megapode (p.157) confined to upland forest on the small island of Waigeo. Another island, Biak, has its own endemic scops-owl, paradise kingfisher, monarch-flycatcher and white-eye, and shares a parrot, the Black-winged Lory, only with other islands in New Guinea's Geelvink Bay; with the exception of the lory, these are all forest birds with limited distributions and at risk from any logging.

To the east of New Guinea, the large island of New Britain, 500 km long and rising to over 2000 m, has several endemics that likewise have the Damoclean sword of deforestation hanging over them. There may be only a few hundred Black Honey-buzzards; the Slaty-backed Goshawk, New Britain Goshawk and New Britain Sparrowhawk are probably not much commoner. The Golden Owl and New Britain King-fisher are evidently also scarce.

A few hundred kilometres to the south, two islands in the d'Entrecasteaux archipelago hold the entire population of Goldie's Bird-of-paradise; and Tagula, in the Louisades, has its own honeyeater and its own butcherbird (one of an Australo-Papuan family, pied or black mostly, that included the currawongs and Australian Magpie). A similar distance to the north of New Britain, the Admiralty and St Matthias Islands have,

respectively, their own pitta and their own fantail-flycatcher, again forest birds of limited distribution.

In the Solomon Islands, an archipelago extending more than 1000 km south-east from New Britain, a whole lot of other scarce or local birds more or less associated with forest are at risk. Both Sanford's Fish-eagle and the Imitator Sparrowhawk probably do not exceed a few hundreds. Woodford's Rail, found on several islands, is threatened by deforestation; even more, the San Cristobal Mountain Rail and Ground-thrush both have a huge logging project hanging over them. Little is known about three or four pigeons, three white-eyes of small islands, the Moustached Kingfisher or the Black-faced Pitta. Other rainforest endemics of the Solomons include the Fearful Owl, two warblers and a monarch-flycatcher. Heinroth's Shearwater, whose nesting-places have not yet been found, is thought to breed on Bougainville.

The arc of islands that begins with the Bismarck archipelago and continues through the Solomons extends to Vanuatu, the Loyalty Islands, New Caledonia and eventually, via Lord Howe and Nor-folk, to New Zealand. In Vanuatu the only species currently causing concern is the Santo Mountain Starling, rediscovered in 1991 after many years without an observation. The Loyalty Islands have two endemic white-eyes on Lifou.

The much larger New Caledonia holds the rema-rkable Kagu (85), a unique bird classed as 'Endan-gered'. Other threatened endemics there include the beautiful Cloven-feathered Dove – emerald-green with yellow belly and shaggy thighs – and the Giant Imperial Pigeon: both are excessively hunted in their forest habitats, which logging and mining have made much more accessible, and are classed as 'Vulnerable'. The Caledonian Greybird (a cuckoo-shrike) and the Red-faced Honeyeater are two more scarce New Caledonian birds.

Finally, in New Zealand and its islands, over 20 birds are causing concern, more than half actually classed as 'Endangered'. A number are seabirds,

90
TAKAHE
Porphyrio mantelli

New Zealand's Takahe, largest of the world's 130 rails and gallinules, probably numbers under 200. Related to the widespread Purple Swamphen, but bigger and bulkier, this huge violet-blue and green 'coot' with massive red bill, thick legs, and white undertail is, like many island rails, flightless. For 50 years to 1948 it was thought extinct; then some were located in tussock grassland on the Murchison and Kepler Mountains, the wildest part of South Island. Survival is aided by the area's inaccessibility and by government protection, with a captive-breeding programme as a safeguard. Introduced mammals are problems, particularly stoats as predators and deer as grazers of the habitat.

including the Yellow-eyed Penguin (**86**); the Westland and Parkinson's Black Petrels (**87**); and several of the smaller gadfly-petrels – among which are Cook's and Pycroft's, on islets off the 'mainland' and the Chatham and Magenta Petrels, on the Chatham Islands.

The last two, like the two black petrels, are 'Endangered'. The Chatham Petrel numbers only a few hundred on one small island, Rangatira. The Magenta Petrel, named not for its colour (mainly brownish-grey with white underbody) but because the original specimen was obtained by the Italian research vessel *Magenta*, was thought extinct for more than a century until a few were rediscovered on the old Chatham Islands breeding site.

This same archipelago holds four other endangered species, three of which are endemic. The Chatham

91
KAKAPO
Strigops habroptilus

*Nocturnal, flightless, up to 3 kg, this is the oddest and
heaviest of parrots. Camouflaged in green and
yellow, barred and mottled, it has an owl-like face
and huge feet. It chews fruits, shoots and roots on the
plant. Noisy only in courtship, the males excavate
'bowls', joined by tracks, to which they attract the
much smaller females by booming calls and dancing
displays. Once widespread in New Zealand's forests,
some 60 now remain, mainly on Stewart Island and
introduced to Little Barrier and Codfish.
Deforestation, hunting, and Man's mammals are to
blame: deer grazing, or trampling the bowls; stoats,
rats, possums and cats preying on birds and nests.
Reproduction, too, is less than annual.*

Oystercatcher has a population of not much more
than 50. The Chatham Snipe is closely related to the
New Zealand Snipe of the Auckland, Snares and
Antipodes island groups: both these small, compact,
relatively short-billed and primitive waders are highly
vulnerable to introduced cats and rats; subspecies on
two other island groups have already been lost. Also
confined to the Chatham Islands are the Chatham
Black Robin (**88**) and the last of the Shore Plovers (**89**)
that were once more widespread in New Zealand.

Restricted to a few islands in an area less than
100 km across in Cook Strait, the New Zealand King
Cormorant is at risk only from its limited range and
rather small numbers which could quickly be affected
by, say, an oiling disaster.

The machinations of the modern world, this time in
the form of hydro-electric schemes, are putting
two other birds of South Island at risk. The smallish

Black-fronted Tern nests locally only by dried rivers and lake shores. The Black Stilt – one of the world's rarest waders, with under 50 remaining – likewise breeds on river shingle and adjacent marshland, and its main area is at risk from flooding; it is also vulnerable to cats and rats and, no less seriously, there is increasing hybridisation with the Australasian Black-winged Stilt, which has benefited from the transformation of New Zealand into farmland.

The Brown Teal is another of New Zealand's interesting relict birds although, as ducks go, it is nothing special to look at. Once widespread throughout the islands, its numbers were greatly reduced by drainage and hunting, by cats and rats on the smaller islands, and perhaps by an introduced poultry disease. The Auckland and Campbell Islands races are flightless and were wiped out by cats on the main islands of those groups, though surviving on outlying islets. Otherwise the biggest numbers are on Great Barrier Island, off North Island.

Several landbirds classed as 'Endangered' include the Takahe (**90**) and the remarkable Kakapo (**91**). The Orange-fronted Parakeet, now reduced to one small area of South Island and listed as 'Endangered', is a colour variety of the Yellow-crowned Parakeet, itself much affected by forest destruction but still not uncommon in mountain areas and on the smaller islands. The related Antipodes Green Parakeet is at risk only because it is confined to a little island about 700 km south-east of New Zealand; were cats to become established there, that could spell the end for this bird, which supplements its diet by feeding on dead penguins.

The Stitchbird, so named from one of its calls, is a nectar-feeder once found in various parts of North Island, but now confined to Little Barrier Island, where it is at some risk from feral cats; this is not one of the more spectacularly coloured honeyeaters, though the male has a black head, white eye-tufts and yellow breast-band.

The Saddleback and the Kokako are the sole surviving relatives of the extinct Huia (*p.152*). These wattlebirds, so called because of the fleshy orange wattle (blue on one race of the Kokako) on each side of the gape, are birds of the forest interior. They epitomise the impact of Man through his felling of the trees and introducing predators and competitors.

Kiwis are perhaps the most celebrated, if actually little known, of New Zealand's birds. Not large (the biggest only 55 cm long and 35 cm high), and flightless and weak-sighted, these mainly nocturnal creatures show no wings or tail and are entirely covered in a shaggy coat of hair-like feathers. Their stout feet are adapted to a terrestrial existence, their long bills to probing for worms and larvae. Each large egg is 20–25 per cent of the female's body weight. The Little Spotted Kiwi, the smallest of the three, was once widespread on North and South Islands but is probably extinct except on Kapiti, in Cook Strait, where it was introduced and where there are now some hundreds.

This demonstrates the present pattern of New Zealand's birds. Although a good deal of original forest has been preserved in the highlands and national parks, many of the forest species of the two main islands are now patchily distributed or even, like the Little Spotted Kiwi and the Saddleback, confined to offshore islands; there they have been introduced or are protected as part of a programme set rolling by the New Zealand Wildlife Service and now continued by the Department of Conservation. Thus, if the great farmlands seem to be dominated by European birds and Common Mynahs, microcosms of New Zealand's heritage can still be found in the reserves, particularly on offshore islands.

Tropical islands of Micronesia and Polynesia

Birds of small islands have suffered more seriously than those of continental regions. Nowhere has this been clearer than among the oceanic islands of the tropical Pacific. Micronesia covers the western tropical Pacific, north of the more continental islands of Melanesia. Polynesia is a triangle with its three corners formed by the Hawaiian group, New Zealand, and isolated Easter Island 1500 km from its nearest neighbour and half as far again from the shores of Chile. But temperate New Zealand, with its dependent islands, is more appropriately part of Australasia (*chapter 7*).

In the tropical Pacific the totals of extinctions and – more important now – of birds endangered are very serious, and the numbers of artificial introductions unparalleled even in New Zealand.

The Pacific Ocean as a whole, from the Aleutians to Antarctica and from the Philippines to Panama, covers 165 million square km. This is almost exactly a third of the world's surface, and more than the total of its land areas; the Atlantic and Indian oceans are each less than half the size. It is also the only ocean that touches on five of the great zoogeographical regions. The continental islands at the fringes of the Pacific, many of which were at one time joined to adjacent landmasses, have been dealt with under those other regions.

The truly oceanic islands of the Pacific – never part of any continental mass above the sea during the geological ages that have seen the emergence of vertebrates in general, and birds and mammals in particular – are all either volcanic in origin or coral atolls formed on sunken ridges. There are more than 10,000 such islands in tropical Micronesia and Polynesia, stretching 12,000 km from the Northern Marianas to

Easter Island. Most are concentrated in the western, central and southern parts of the open Pacific.

They include the Micronesian archipelagos of the North Marianas (taking in Guam), Palau, the Carolines (used loosely to cover all the islands from Yap to Kosrae), Wake, the Marshalls, and Nauru; Fiji, which is intermediate between Melanesia and Polynesia; the Hawaiian Islands in north Polynesia; and the central and eastern Polynesian groups of Kiribati (formerly Gilbert, Phoenix and Line Islands), Tuvalu (Ellice), Tokelau, Samoa, Tonga, Cook, Society Islands, Tubuai (Austral), Tuamotu, Marquesas, and Gambier and Pitcairn to Easter Island.

Nearly all are strictly tropical – between the Tropics of Cancer and Capricorn – but the northern Hawaiian Islands and a few groups in the extreme south, including Rapa Iti, Pitcairn and Easter Island itself, lie just outside. The arcs of Melanesian islands that include the Solomons, Vanuatu and New Caledonia represent the easternmost of the New Guinea folds and are here treated as part of Australasia (*chapter 7*).

Much of Micronesia and Polynesia are thought to have been the last habitable areas to be colonised by Man. Melanesia was settled over 30,000 years ago, when Australia and New Guinea were still joined. Much later, the Pacific islands were colonised gradually by a mixture of Caucasians from Asia and, later, Negroid Melanesians. The Bismarck archipelago is thought to have been settled in about 2000 BC and Fiji, Tonga and Samoa by 1000 BC.

These great ocean-travelling peoples then dispersed to Micronesia and eastern Polynesia, reaching the Marquesas before 100 BC and, from there, Hawaii by around AD 300, but not Easter Island until the eighth century at the earliest. It was then another thousand years before the first Europeans followed and began to wreak more havoc through intensive deforestation and the introduction of alien animals and disease. The worst damage has been done in the last 250 years.

Most of these oceanic islands are small and their total landmass covers around 47,000 square km – or less than one-thirtieth of one per cent of the whole Pacific. More than half of this land area is made up by just three of the 10,000 islands. The largest two, Hawaii itself and Fiji's Viti Levu, are each smaller than Yorkshire and not much more than half the size of Wales or, moving across the Atlantic, smaller than Jamaica and one-fifteenth as big as Florida. The third largest, Vanua Levu in Fiji, is only half the size of the first two and, next in order, there are a mere half-dozen (including three more of the Hawaiian group) between 1000 and 2000 square km. The tenth largest is only 670 square km and the twentieth 260 square km.

Despite their small size, a number of the volcanic islands have high peaks and ridges, and steep cliffs. Hawaii itself rises in two peaks, Mauna Kea and

92
GUAM RAIL
Rallus owstoni

Though weak-looking fliers, rails colonised many islands and often evolved into new species. Terrestrial, some lost all powers of flight. Man arrived with his cats and rats, and a lot of rails became extinct: 14 since 1600. But Guam's flightless rail – the size of a short-billed Water Rail, barred below, with rusty head, and grey brows and chest – was a survivor. Although hunted for food and caught in rat traps, it flourished. A forest bird, it even adapted to grassland and fed on road-kills. Post-war estimates quadrupled to 80,000 by 1968. But now, introduced tree-snakes have devastated many Guam birds, so this rail is being bred in captivity and introduced to Rota, 100 km to the north.

Mauna Loa, to over 4000 m; and Maui to 3060 m. Tahiti reaches over 2200 m, and another dozen Pacific islands have peaks over 1000 m. Some Pacific volcanoes are recent or still active. Older islands are, or were, heavily forested.

In the Indian Ocean, the very large island of Madagascar (twelve times as big as all the tropical archipelagos of the oceanic Pacific put together) is in quite a different category from the small oceanic island

93
HAWAIIAN GOOSE
Branta sandvicensis

Endemic to Hawaii and Maui, this grey-brown goose with a dark-grooved buff neck and black hood is almost a success story. In the late 1700s there were perhaps 25,000, but introduced mammals, hunting, and loss of habitat to ranching and agriculture had almost wiped them out by 1950. Captive-breeding, notably at Slimbridge, has enabled 2000 to be put back since 1960, but the numbers are not self-sustaining and still total only a few hundreds. Apart from mongooses and other predators, problems may include food supply, disease or inbreeding. The Ne-ne (a local name from its 'nay-nay' call) now lives on volcanic slopes with thin vegetation; its feet are not fully webbed, and it swims little.

groups of the Malagasy region. In the Pacific, although the Hawaiian Islands are a long way from all others and quite unique for various reasons, even they are relatively small, with the characteristically restricted avifaunas of such islands.

The vast expanses of this section of the Pacific make for an oceanic as much as a tropical climate, with evenly high humidity and temperatures through the year. Air circulation, however, produces significant differences in weather patterns across the region, and rainfall figures are affected as much by an island's longitude, size and height as by its latitude; windward sides of mountainous islands are the wettest.

From the central Pacific eastwards the north-east and south-east trade winds bring a mixture of sunshine and showers with periodic downpours. Around the equator itself, in the doldrums, there is little wind and much cloud. The western Pacific, on the other hand, is a zone of monsoon winds produced by Asia's seasonal temperature changes – north-west from November to March and south-east in the rest of the year.

Typhoons, with torrential rains and mountainous seas, cause much damage in western Micronesia in July–November and, south of the equator, also occur as far east as the Society Islands in the early part of the year. Sometimes, there are long periods of drought on low islands. In the early 1980s, for example, the entire western Pacific suffered drought, while islands in the east were subjected to exceptional rain.

It is now well recognised that the number of species on an island varies reasonably closely with its size. In rough terms, one can expect that a ten-fold decrease in size – from, say, 1000 square km to 100 square km, or from 100 square km to 10 square km – will result in a halving of the number of species, or vice versa. This has to do with area (and so of sample size), diversity of habitat, and interspecific competition. It is of course affected by latitude (with larger numbers of landbird species in the tropics) and by remoteness (isolated islands far from continents or archipelagos having lower colonisation), but it is a useful rule of thumb.

Over 400 species are recorded in tropical Melanesia and Polynesia, but these include many migrants (especially seabirds, herons, wildfowl and waders) and introduced birds. For example, the Hawaiian group has more than 260 species recorded, but almost 50 of those are introductions and about 115 are passage migrants and vagrants; 15 or more endemics are now extinct. Nevertheless, 230 indigenous species breed in the tropical Pacific, of which 165 are endemic to the region and often to single island groups.

Introductions

Interspecific competition relates to the balance between rates of immigration and extinction, which raises the question of the impact of naturalised birds.

Apart from introducing rats, cats, dogs, mongooses, deer, rabbits and various other mammals that prey on birds, or attack their nests and young, or overgraze the habitat, or compete for food – as well as, disastrously, snakes and disease-bearing mosquitoes (*pp.171–3*) – European Man has long taken familiar or colourful birds with him to the distant islands that he has colonised. Unfortunately, many of these have had a serious effect on indigenous species. Chapter 7 showed the extent to which introduced birds have come to dominate the avifauna of New Zealand.

With the exceptions of the widely naturalised Rock Pigeons, Common Starlings, House Sparrows and, more regionally, Common Pheasants, bird introductions have had little effect on the indigenous bird populations of the major continents. On the other hand, in Seychelles (*chapter 5*), for example, the three commonest landbirds have all been introduced and compete with endemics.

In the Pacific islands in general, and the Hawaiian group in particular, the situation is far worse. At one time or another, over 150 species of birds have been introduced to the Pacific region, either intentionally or from accidental escapes of cagebirds. Many of the latter probably did not even nest ferally and a majority died out – some quickly, but others not for several

decades. But over 60 species are now completely naturalised. Almost 50 of these are found in one or more of the Hawaiian islands, all but about a dozen of them nowhere else in the Pacific.

Taking the Hawaiian group alone first, approximate first dates of introduction are available for many of the species. About a quarter were brought in during or before the nineteenth century and the first two decades

94

TUAMOTU SANDPIPER
Prosobonia cancellatus

This small, dark brown wader – barred and streaky, with thin creamy eyebrows – lives only on a few uninhabited atolls in the mid-Pacific Tuamotu Islands; formerly it occurred over more than 3500 km between Kiritimati and the Gambiers. Using its short thin bill to pick up insects in coral rubble and leaf litter on and behind the open shore, it is tame, inquisitive, and vulnerable to introduced cats and rats. They doubtless caused its decline, though many sandpipers were shot by collectors. Its only close relative, the Tahiti Sandpiper – similar but plain brown above and reddish below, with a white band on the shoulders – was extinct within a few decades of European colonisation.

95
POLYNESIAN GROUND-DOVE
Gallicolumba erythroptera

*There are over 50 ground-doves and quail-doves:
most are small, many are island forms and, as they
are terrestrial – often even nesting on or close to the
ground – they fall to introduced cats and rats. Nearly
a third of all the ground-doves now seem at risk. This
species belongs to a genus found mainly in
Australasian and Pacific archipelagos. Formerly on
Tahiti and other Society Islands where now
apparently extinct, it is confined to several
uninhabited atolls of the Tuamotu group to the
north-east; there it may be quite numerous. The
purple and black male is striking, with white face and
chest; the brownish-grey female rather less so, with
grey head, pale eyebrows and rusty breast.*

of the twentieth. Otherwise there were two main
periods of introductions, more than a dozen species
being established between 1920 and the early 1930s
(especially 1928–31) and a similar number between
1957 and the early 1970s (especially about 1957–66).
Three of the established species originated from
Central or South America, nine or ten each from North
America and Africa, and over 25 from Asia, especially
in the south-east.

Apart from feral Junglefowls, Indian Peafowls,
Common Pheasants and Common Turkeys – as well as
various quails, prairie-chickens and the Helmeted
Guineafowl that never, or only briefly, became established – eight of Hawaii's naturalised birds are gamebirds (francolins, partridges, American and Old World
quails, and the Kalij Pheasant); and, in addition to
Feral Rock Pigeons, three are doves.

The rest include Chestnut-bellied Sandgrouse; three
parrots; Common Barn-owl (otherwise indigenous in

the Pacific from Fiji to Samoa and Tonga); Sky Lark; two Indian bulbuls, notably the Red-vented; Northern Mockingbird; Japanese Bush-warbler and White-eye; four laughingthrushes and other babblers; Common Mynah; House Sparrow; nine waxbills and mannikins; four American sparrows and buntings; three finches; and Northern Cardinal and Western Meadowlark.

A number of these are now common. Grey Francolin, Barred Ground-dove, Sky Lark, Japanese Bush-warbler, Common Mynah, House Sparrow, Indian Silverbill, Nutmeg and Chestnut Mannikins, Java Sparrow, and House Finch are 'abundant' on at least one (and often all) of Hawaii's six main islands of Kauai, Oahu, Molokai, Lanai, Maui and Hawaii itself. And, since it was first introduced on Oahu in 1930, the Japanese White-eye has become probably the most numerous of all Hawaiian birds.

In contrast, a few have been well established and then decreased or disappeared. For example, the babbler burdened with the name Red-billed Leiothrix was abundant between the 1920s and 1940s, but has since declined, and on Kauai and Oahu is now rare. Similarly, the Varied Tit of Japan was once naturalised on those same two islands, but had disappeared completely by the early 1960s.

About a dozen of the birds introduced to Hawaii have been naturalised in one or more other Pacific island groups, along with at least 15 further species. Fiji with nine, the Northern Marianas (especially Guam) and Society Islands with eight each, and the Carolines with six, are the archipelagos most afflicted, but the Tonga, Samoa, Cook, Tubuai and Marquesas groups, and isolated Easter Island, all have a few.

The additional introduced birds in one or more of these areas include Brown Quails in Fiji and Blue-breasted on Guam; Philippine Turtle-doves in the Marianas (including Guam); Sulphur-crested Cockatoos and Eclectus Parrots on Palau; Silver-eyes (from New Zealand) in the Society and Tubuai Islands (otherwise indigenous in Fiji); Black Drongos in the Marianas (including Guam); Australian Magpies on Taveuni, Fiji; Common Starlings in Fiji and Tonga; Jungle Mynahs on Viti Levu, Fiji, and Upolu, Samoa; Tree Sparrows on the Marianas (including Guam) and single islands of the Marshalls and Carolines; Red-browed Waxbills in the Society Islands and Marquesas; Hunstein's Mannikins on Pohnpei, and Chestnut-breasted in the Society Islands and Marquesas; and Crimson-backed Tanagers on Tahiti. More unexpected was the establishment on Easter Island of Chimango Caracaras – scavenging raptors from South America – and Chilean Tinamous.

Many of the introduced species on these smaller islands are uncommon or local, but the Black Drongo is 'abundant' in the Marianas, as is the Red Avadavat (one of the waxbill-mannikin group also introduced to Hawaii) on the main islands of Fiji; and the Common Mynah dominates almost everywhere (even though it died out on Kwajalein in the Marshall Islands).

Nevertheless, any introduced birds on small islands, even if they are neither predators nor direct competitors, are bound to constrict the niches of the often delicately balanced endemics.

Extinctions

About 25 – almost exactly one-quarter – of the world total of just over a hundred bird species known to have become extinct since 1600 were endemic to one or more of the tropical Pacific islands. This means 25 per cent of the extinctions from 0·03 per cent of the land area.

In fact, considering the tiny sizes of most of these specks of land in the open Pacific and the threats everywhere to island birds, particularly from introductions of all kinds and from deforestation or other habitat destruction, this is perhaps not such a large number. At least 30 others have been lost from the more continental and often much bigger islands at the edges of the Pacific, including New Zealand (*chapter 7*); these bring the total extinctions for the whole Pacific to about 55. And 24 have gone since 1600 from the far less numerous islands of the Malagasy region (*chapter 5*). It is sobering to realise that four-fifths of all known bird extinctions in the past four hundred years have involved island species of the tropical and southern temperate regions; the Caribbean islands actually lost more of theirs before 1600 (*chapter 2*).

In the tropical Pacific, it is more important now that over twice as many as are already extinct – another 60 endemic species, as well as a number of distinctive island races – are already regarded as 'Vulnerable', 'Rare' or, in many cases, critically 'Endangered'. The following summary of extinctions does, however, help to drive home what is going to happen to many of those others unless conservation and education succeed.

The great majority of the total losses have been from the Hawaiian Islands. Half of some 15 birds that have disappeared there since 1600 – most since 1890 and some since 1960 – belonged to the endemic family of Hawaiian honeycreepers (*see* **99**). Many of these became extinct in the 1890s and the first decade of the twentieth century, but the straight-billed scarlet Kaka-wahie, or Molokai Creeper, was last recorded as recently as 1963 and the sickle-billed greenish Kauai Akialoa also in the 1960s: these two little birds may perhaps still exist in the uplands of Molokai and Kauai, though it is thought unlikely.

Other lost birds of this string of islands were the Hawaiian Rail (1884) and the Laysan Rail (early 1920s, though surviving until 1944 through introductions on Midway); the Amaui, a solitaire thrush of Oahu (1820s); two of the four yellow-patched blackish honeyeaters with the name oo ('o-o') that make up an endemic genus (the Hawaii Oo survived until 1934 and perhaps could still exist?); and a larger streaky honeyeater, the Kioea (1860s). To this group may be added the Laysan form of the Millerbird, a brown and white brush-warbler that disappeared on Laysan by the early 1920s, though it survives as an endangered if not uncommon species 1800 km away on Nihoa, its last refuge.

Most of the remaining extinctions were on the Caroline and Society Islands: more rails, a wader, two parakeets and one or probably two starlings. The Wake Rail failed to survive the Second World War on Wake Island; it thus followed into oblivion the tiny black Kosrae Crake of the Carolines (known only from the original specimens taken in 1827) and the Samoan Woodhen, a small black gallinule that once lived on Savaii but has not been seen since 1908. The White-winged or Tahitian Sandpiper, a close relative of the endangered Tuamotu Sandpiper (*see* **94**), was identified from three specimens collected on Tahiti and Moorea in the Society Islands by Cook's expedition in 1773, but, as with the Kosrae Crake, the arrival of Man and his ship's rats proved too much: the species was never seen again.

The Society Islands were also the home of the Raiatea Parakeet, similarly known only from the original two specimens taken in 1773, and the related Black-fronted Parakeet that survived until 1844. The two starlings, belonging to an Indomalayan and Australasian genus that has evolved a number of island species in the Pacific, were endemic to the Caroline Islands: the large Kosrae Mountain Starling, again known only from the original specimens of 1828, and the much smaller Pohnpei Mountain Starling, not seen since 1956 despite subsequent surveys.

It looks, however, as if Guam, an unincorporated territory of the USA between the Northern Marianas and the Carolines, is now heading up the list of 'extinction islands' (*p.14*). Already the little Guam Flycatcher, widespread and common in the mid 1970s but 'Endangered' a decade later, has been lost.

Threatened birds

Directly or indirectly, Man has caused almost all of these extinctions on small islands. Hunting for food is unlikely to have been a factor in most cases, though uncontrolled shooting on many islands is now a real threat to some endangered birds. Hunting for feather adornments has also played its part, and the taking of eggs of seabirds and megapodes is another hazard for some rare or local species.

More serious has been the destruction of upland habitats, particularly of primary forest, and this continues today. It may take the form of logging, or of grazing of the understorey by introduced sheep, pigs, goats and deer. And it is of course the introductions of competitors, predators and disease that have done the greatest damage to some species.

In Hawaii, where mosquitoes were first introduced in the 1820s, the diseases they transferred from introduced birds to indigenous species, which had no immunity, are considered to have been the reason for sudden declines in the lowland populations of landbirds on all the main islands between about 1860 and 1920. Now, many endemic species are found only above 600 m, the limit of the mosquito-infestation.

A comparable crash has affected the birds of Guam since the 1970s. After surviving habitat destructions, various animal introductions and the Second World War, many have suddenly declined catastrophically.

96

TOOTH-BILLED PIGEON
Didunculus strigirostris

This large, thickset, short-tailed, greeny-black and chestnut pigeon, endemic to Western Samoa, was once thought to link pigeons with dodos: its Latin name means 'owl-billed little dodo'. Its red and yellow bill has almost a parrot-like look: upper mandible hooked, lower notched with 'teeth'. Juveniles are barred red-brown, and dark-billed, but the same shape. Like many pigeons, the Tooth-billed feeds both in trees and on the ground; it is shy and a strong flier, taking off with loud claps, but it is traditionally hunted and already rare. Restricted to upland forest on Savaii and Upolu, it is threatened now by felling to meet the financial and pastural needs of a growing human population.

97

ULTRAMARINE LORIKEET
Vini ultramarina

*Lorikeets are small to medium-sized Australasian and Pacific parrots. This one, only 2 cm
longer than a sparrow, is shades of blue above and mottled white below, with an orange-red
bill; rear crown, breast-band and thighs are tinged mauve. Endemic to two islands of the
mid-Pacific Marquesas and introduced on a third, only a few hundreds remain, mostly on Ua
Pou. They live from sea-level to mountain ridges among tall flowering or fruiting trees, but
the forests are in decline. Restless, noisy with screeching whistles, pairs and parties clamber
about the canopy, then dash to another tree. Lorikeets have special brush-tipped tongues for
pollen and nectar, but also eat fruits, seeds and insects.*

Although mosquitoes have long been present, avian diseases are not apparently involved. Instead, it is the result of the accidental introduction of predatory brown tree-snakes, which in a couple of decades have multiplied rapidly and now infest all the island's forest. The tiny Guam Flycatcher has already gone for ever and the Guam Rail (**92**) is now 'Endangered'; so is the Marianas Crow, otherwise found only on Rota. Also endangered are Guam's endemic populations of Moorhen, White-throated Ground-dove, Marianas Fruit-dove, Island Swiftlet, Micronesian Kingfisher, Rufous Fantail, Micronesian Starling, Micronesian Honeyeater, and Bridled White-eye.

In all, over 60 species of tropical Pacific birds and a number of endemic races are variously regarded as being at risk and in many cases actually 'Endangered'.

Among the 60 are several seabirds that have the advantage of ability to range over the ocean, but are open to many of the same threats as landbirds during the breeding season. The Hawaiian Petrel is not confined to those islands, but also nests 7000 km away on Galápagos: once common and widespread, it has declined in both areas through disturbance, capture for food, and predations by introduced mammals and is now classed as 'Endangered'; it does still, however, nest on two or three islands of Hawaii and four or five of Galápagos.

The all-dark Murphy's Petrel apparently breeds only on several islands in the Tubuai, Tuamotu and Pitcairn groups, but may be commoner than thought. The Fiji Petrel, also all-dark, is known only from an old specimen and four recent captures of disoriented birds: this species is presumed to nest on Gau and is evidently rare. Newell's Shearwater, breeding only on forested slopes on three or four islands of Hawaii has greatly decreased through disturbance and predation, so that it is now regarded as seriously threatened.

Even without the 'Marianas Mallard' – which is, or more probably was, a hybrid population of Mallard and Grey or Pacific Black Duck ancestry in the Northern Mariana Islands – there are three threatened wildfowl in the Pacific; two are sometimes treated as small races of the Mallard, but differ in various ways.

The Hawaiian Duck, which looks like a small female Mallard, was formerly widespread but, apart from reintroduced stock on Hawaii and Oahu, is now only on Kauai, and 'Endangered'. The Laysan Duck – dark red-brown with white on the head – is endemic to the far-out Hawaiian island of Laysan. Like the Hawaiian Goose (**93**), it represents a conservation success story after the population had been reduced to a handful, first by shooting and then through the destruction of much of the island's vegetation by introduced rabbits; from a single fertilised female, many have been bred in captivity and, with releases back, the island population has now stabilised at about 500 – but it remains 'Rare'.

Apart from the Hawaiian Hawk, a smallish buzzard of forested or tree-scattered uplands on Hawaii itself, the non-passerine landbirds at risk in the Pacific are almost all megapodes, rails, pigeons, small parrots, swifts, and kingfishers.

Megapodes are mainly Australasian (*chapter 7*), but the Maleo (*see* **68**) and others are Indomalayan and two live on Pacific islands. The Micronesian Scrubfowl is confined to Palau and the Marianas, and common only on uninhabited islands; its eggs are harvested and, though that in itself may not be too serious, cats and other introduced predators are a grave danger to this beach-nesting species. Pritchard's Scrubfowl, endemic to the isolated Tongan island of Niuafo'ou, between Fiji and Samoa (though now also introduced to Tafahi 200 km to the east), has a tiny range and also suffers some egg-harvesting, but appears to be holding its own, perhaps because it lays in what may be less accessible tunnels in volcanic ash near steam vents.

Like the Guam Rail, the larger and very different Bar-winged Rail of Fiji is classed as 'Endangered' because of its small numbers – indeed, it was thought extinct for nearly a century until its rediscovery in 1973 on Viti Levu – and its vulnerability to introduced rats, cats and mongooses.

The Henderson Rail is one of four birds endemic to the small, flat-topped and steep-sided Henderson Island, which lies north-east of Pitcairn and holds what is among the world's least damaged island communities. This rail is common – perhaps as many as 20,000 pairs – but it has a tiny range in island forest that has as yet had little exposure to disturbance and introductions. With its black plumage and red eyes and legs, it is not unlike a large edition of the extinct Kosrae Crake – and remember how quickly that disappeared when Man came along.

The peculiar Hawaiian Coot – dimorphic with a large frontal shield that is either white or, less commonly, red – has a population still in the thousands, but is regarded as 'Endangered'. Another vulnerable water-associated landbird is the small Tuamotu Sandpiper (**94**).

Pigeons and doves are among the great colonists of oceanic islands and, aside from introductions, some 30 species are found in the tropical Pacific, many of them endemic to single archipelagos. The Polynesian Ground-dove (**95**), now confined to uninhabited Tuamotu atolls, and the rare and remarkable Tooth-billed Pigeon (**96**) are two examples of more than half-a-dozen that appear at risk through shooting, deforestation and habitat disturbance, and in some cases introduced predators.

Other threatened pigeons include the Marquesas Ground-dove (endemic to two uninhabited islands), the Marquesas Imperial Pigeon (on Nukuhiva only and classed as 'Endangered'), the Polynesian Imperial Pigeon (very rare on Tahiti and otherwise only on Makatéa in the Tuamotu group), and the Marianas and Rapa Fruit-doves.

The last is very rare and endemic to Rapa, south of Tahiti, where a population of 274 is estimated in the remaining fragmented forest totalling 292 ha. Four more of the 15 Pacific fig-eating fruit-doves – typically green and often with grey heads and red to purple or lavender caps – are found on only one or two islands, and therefore vulnerable to any disaster (such as fire) or major change (such as deforestation).

Parrots have also been good colonists of tropical islands, and there are more than a dozen species in the Pacific. Many are lories, small to medium-sized species that feed on pollen and nectar and are mostly brightly coloured. The only ones thought to be at risk are the Ultramarine Lorikeet (**97**) of the Marquesas and the Blue Lorikeet (with a white breast) of Tuamotu and the Society Islands, which has also been introduced to Aitutaki in the Cook Islands.

The latter in particular lives in coconut palms and so has no shortage of habitat, but both have declined or disappeared from some islands, while remaining more numerous elsewhere. It has been suggested that they may have been affected by the introduction of mosquitoes carrying avian malaria, but in that case two rarer species – the Red-throated Lorikeet of montane rainforest on Fiji and another endemic of tiny Henderson Island, Stephen's Lorikeet – could easily be at much greater risk.

Swifts are great travellers, some continental species migrating vast distances between the two hemispheres, but few live on oceanic islands. The main exceptions are the small cave swiftlets related to the Edible-nest Swiftlet of bird's-nest-soup fame. Five swiftlets breed within the tropical Pacific region and, apart from the Guam race of the Island Swiftlet now classed as 'Endangered', two species may be at some risk because of their restricted ranges and small populations.

The Tahiti Swiftlet, of Tahiti and Moorea in the Society Islands, is now rare and local. The very similar Sawtell's Swiftlet, not identified until 1973 and confined to Atiu in the Cook Islands, is only in small numbers but apparently stable. Island swiftlets nest mostly in tight colonies in hidden underground caves and, in general, are little threatened except by excessive disturbance, intentional vandalism and, possibly, introduced predators.

The kingfishers of the Pacific – mostly blue above and white or rufous below – are complicated, because it is far from clear which should be treated as species and which as races. All belong to the 'collared' group

98

PALILA
Psittirostra bailleui

*This large finch-like bird is in fact a Hawaiian honeycreeper, near the other end of the
range of adaptive radiation from the Akiapolaau (**99**). Holding mamane pods in its feet, it
uses its short deep bill to tear them open and crush the seeds. The yellow head and breast,
black mask, grey back, and white belly are only slightly duller on the female. Endemic to
Hawaii itself, a fluctuating population of a few thousands, often in small flocks outside the
breeding season, lives above 2000 m on Mauna Kea, the northern peak. It is endangered
because the mamane forests are being degraded by the erosion and lack of regeneration
resulting from overgrazing by goats, sheep and pigs.*

175

99

EVOLUTION OF HAWAIIAN HONEYCREEPERS, AND THE AKIAPOLAAU
Hemignathus munroi

Many Hawaiian birds have Polynesian names, often onomatopoeic renderings of songs or calls. None seems more complex to the English ear than those of the Hawaiian honeycreepers. Confusingly, these birds are not closely related either to the Central and South American honeycreepers, which are tanagers, or to the Australasian and Pacific honeyeaters. They are usually placed in an endemic family of their own.

Of 27–29 species, at least seven and probably nine are extinct – mostly in the 20 years around the turn of the century, but two in the 1960s. Many of the others are more or less at risk, 13 now classed by the Fish & Wildlife Service as 'Endangered'.

One of the most remarkable is the Akiapolaau ('ah-kee-ah-*po-la*-ow', emphasised on the penultimate two syllables). This stocky little bird – sparrow-sized, large-headed and short-tailed – has an astonishing bill with long curved upper and half-length straight lower mandibles, the latter fully closing only at base and tip. The lower is a stout chisel that, with the upper raised rather awkwardly out of the way, is used on its own to prise open cracks in the bark; the sickle-like upper mandible is then brought into play, again on its own, to hook out insect larvae.

The male is mainly yellow with a green back and black patches in front of the eyes; the dull grey-green female and juveniles have grey by the eyes, and rather smaller (though similar) bills. Often a male is accompanied by two such duller birds. Endangered, like so many Hawaiian species, this one numbers no more than 1500, mostly in two areas of upland forest.

The three-in-one bill – chisel, probe, and pincers – is unique. The related Nukupuu ('noo-koo-*poo*-oo'), also endangered, is similar but for its short lower mandible's being curved to fit the long upper; once widespread, it is now reduced to small populations, 300 km apart, on Maui and Kauai. Four others of this genus are mostly greener (one yellow) with short downcurved bills, but the Akialoa – probably extinct, though perhaps still existing on Kauai – had a much longer, if far less unequal, bill more than a third of its total length.

In radiation of bill-shape and behaviour, the Hawaiian honeycreepers are even more remarkable than Darwin's finches on the Galápagos. A few million years ago, finch-like ancestors are supposed to have arrived in the 1500-km Hawaiian chain where, with few small landbird competitors, their descendants colonised and recolonised the islands, forming new species to fill available niches. The Laysan Finch, westernmost of today's honeycreepers, is perhaps most like the originals. But so varied is this family that its main groups of species were once thought unrelated.

Apart from the Akiapolaau, several with very different bills creep about on trunks like nuthatches, even hang upside down like parrots. But the three main types are: largish heavy-billed 'finches' (*see* **98**) with yellow or red heads and canary-like songs; curve-billed 'sunbirds', mainly red or black with some yellow or white, and squeaky whistled notes; and thin-billed 'warblers', mainly small and greenish. Two of four red species have the most varied songs: one, the Apapane, is the commonest of Hawaii's indigenous birds.

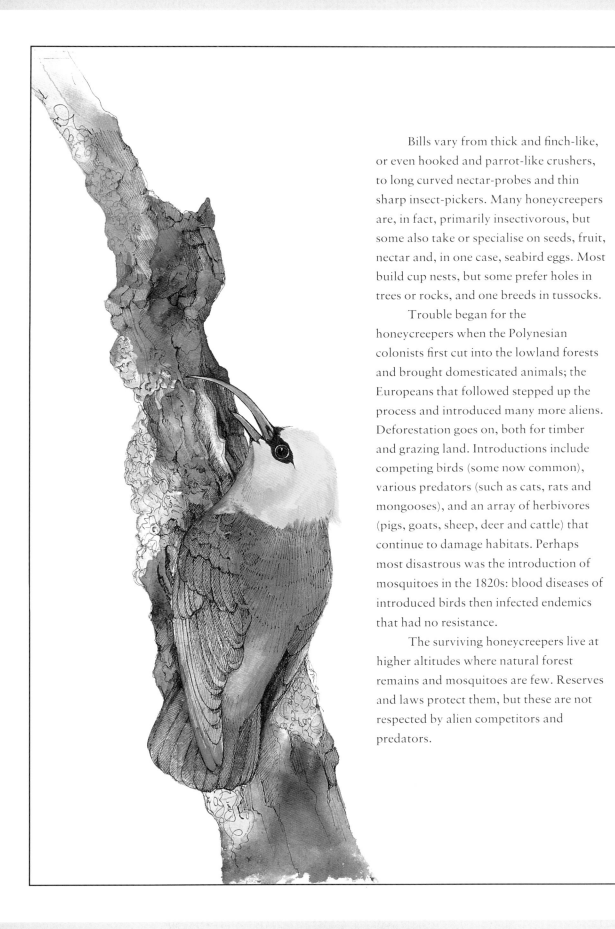

Bills vary from thick and finch-like, or even hooked and parrot-like crushers, to long curved nectar-probes and thin sharp insect-pickers. Many honeycreepers are, in fact, primarily insectivorous, but some also take or specialise on seeds, fruit, nectar and, in one case, seabird eggs. Most build cup nests, but some prefer holes in trees or rocks, and one breeds in tussocks.

Trouble began for the honeycreepers when the Polynesian colonists first cut into the lowland forests and brought domesticated animals; the Europeans that followed stepped up the process and introduced many more aliens. Deforestation goes on, both for timber and grazing land. Introductions include competing birds (some now common), various predators (such as cats, rats and mongooses), and an array of herbivores (pigs, goats, sheep, deer and cattle) that continue to damage habitats. Perhaps most disastrous was the introduction of mosquitoes in the 1820s: blood diseases of introduced birds then infected endemics that had no resistance.

The surviving honeycreepers live at higher altitudes where natural forest remains and mosquitoes are few. Reserves and laws protect them, but these are not respected by alien competitors and predators.

100
RAROTONGA MONARCH
Pomarea dimidiata

*The monarchs – mostly Afrotropical, Australasian and Pacific – are a large group of flycatcher-like birds that may be more closely related to drongos and crows. Two dozen are among the tropical Pacific's most characteristic small birds, very noisy with chattering and trilling calls, and high whistled songs. Endemic to Rarotonga in the Cook Islands, this one is restricted to thick undergrowth in upland forest gullies – steadfastly unable to adapt to secondary woodland – and rare. Very vulnerable to introduced rats and cats, it was evidently already uncommon a century ago; now the total population is 35 or so. Males are slate-grey and white; females, as shown here, are bright rufous, like the immatures (c.f **101**).*

of a large genus of noisy forest kingfishers that feed on insects, crabs, other invertebrates, frogs, and even small reptiles, birds and mammals as much as on fish. There may be anything up to eight or nine species in the Pacific region, including six or seven forms endemic to single islands or archipelagos in Micronesia and between Samoa and the Marquesas. Deforestation is a Damoclean threat to all the species, though some adapt readily to coconut plantations.

The Micronesian Kingfisher is threatened only on Guam and otherwise found on Palau and the Caroline Islands. Most at risk are probably the Mangaia Kingfisher, endemic to that one of the Cook Islands, and the Tuamotu Kingfisher, now confined to Niau (it formerly extended to Mangareva). Both have tiny ranges, and the also rare Marquesas Kingfisher has very little more scope.

If rails, pigeons, parrots, swiftlets and kingfishers are among the widest distributed families of tropical island landbirds, so too are such passerines as monarch-flycatchers, warblers (especially brush-warblers), white-eyes, and starlings. Indeed, if we exclude the rather special case of the Hawaiian honeycreepers, 15 of which are now classed as 'Endangered' (if not, in two cases, already extinct) – see the Palila (**98**) and the Akiapolaau (**99**) – three-quarters of the Pacific passerines at risk belong to these groups.

The monarch-flycatchers are a widespread Old World tropical family typified here by the rare and vulnerable Rarotonga Monarch (**100**) and the seriously endangered Tahiti Monarch (**101**). The Guam Fly-catcher has gone (*p.170*), but upwards of 20 other monarchs are endemic to the Pacific, two-thirds of them in the southern archipelagos from Fiji to the Marquesas. Another classed as 'Endangered' is the much larger Truk Monarch – males of which are mainly white, and females slate – restricted to the Truk group in the Carolines. Two others of the Marquesas, the Marquesas and Iphis Monarchs, are also declining. Against this, some monarchs restricted to just one or two small islands – such as the Tinian Monarch and

the Versicolour Flycatcher, respectively on two islands in the Marianas and on Ogea in Fiji – seem safer than used to be thought.

Among 'Endangered' reed-warblers, the Nihoa Millerbird and the Nauru Reed-warbler are endemic to the islands whose names they bear, the former in Hawaii and the latter south-east of the Carolines. The Nauru bird is sometimes treated as a race of the Nightingale Reed-warbler of the Marianas and Carolines, so called for its particularly long, complicated and melodious song; the Millerbird's Laysan relative is already extinct (*p.170*). Elsewhere, both races of the Tahiti Reed-warbler are rare and the Moorea form particularly threatened. Another 'Endangered' warbler, Fiji's large and mainly red-brown Long-legged Warbler (which has a long tail too), was thought extinct for nearly 70

101

TAHITI MONARCH
Pomarea nigra

This monarch-flycatcher is endemic to the Society Islands, but extinct on Maupiti and now confined to Tahiti, where it is rare and classed as 'Endangered': few have been seen in recent years. It differs curiously from the slightly smaller Rarotonga Monarch (100) in that the female resembles the male, not the young: both adults are black with bluish bills and legs, and only the immatures are cinnamon to rufous, paler below. The Tahiti Monarch lives in dense forest above 700 m, rarely coming into the open. Although noisy, monarchs move through the canopy or undergrowth with flicking wings and fanning tails, and forage by picking insects off leaves and twigs rather than by aerial sallies.

102
SMALL KAUAI THRUSH
Myadestes palmeri

*Akin to the American solitaires, the four small
Hawaiian thrushes are accomplished songsters of
forest undergrowth, often by streams. Three are
endangered from Man's introductions (**99**). With a
distinctive habit of shivering their wings, adults are
brown above and grey below, but this is a juvenile: all
spotty, like many young thrushes, with buff tips
above and dark-edged feathers below. The Puaiohi,
to use its local name, is the smallest; adults have pale
cheeks and pink legs. It and the dark-legged and
shorter-billed Large Kauai Thrush, or Kamao, which
has decreased drastically, are endemic to Kauai,
westernmost of the larger islands, and now restricted
to the reserve of Alakai swamp.*

years until local populations were rediscovered on Viti
Levu and Vanua Levu.

The superficially warbler-like but unrelated white-
eyes – great island birds (*see also* **55**) – are represented
by more than a dozen species in the western and
southern Pacific (and by the abundant introduced
Japanese White-eye throughout the Hawaiian group).
Many are found on only one island or archipelago, but
most are common enough. The Samoan White-eye of
the mountains of Savaii is rare, however, while two of
the four relatively large and atypical white-eyes of
Palau to Pohnpei, in the area of the Caroline Islands,
are 'Endangered'.

One of these, the Great Truk White-eye, is found
mainly at the summit of Tol, the largest island in the
Truk group. The Long-billed White-eye, of Pohnpei,
the next main archipelago to the east, is widespread
but classed as 'Rare' and probably endangered.

The starlings of the Pacific belong to a particular genus that is otherwise confined to Australasia and, marginally, the Indomalayan region. Half-a-dozen are found in the Pacific islands, though the Pohnpei Mountain Starling, like the Kosrae Mountain Starling – both of the Caroline Islands – is very probably already extinct (*p.170*). Of the rest, the Polynesian and the Micronesian Starlings are both widespread and common (except for the latter's endemic Guam race), and the large sooty Samoan Starling is common enough even though confined to Samoa. But the once abundant, if shy, Rarotonga Starling of Rarotonga in the Cook Islands has dropped to around 100 in what is left of the primary forest.

There remain one or two thrushes, honeyeaters, crows and finches. Three of the four thrushes endemic to the Hawaiian Islands – including the Small Kauai Thrush (**102**) – are 'Endangered', like so many Hawaiian species, to the extent of being reduced to a few, or at most a few dozen, birds.

Equally 'Endangered' are the last two of the five or six endemic Hawaiian honeyeaters (*see also p.170*). The small black Kauai Oo was still common enough at the turn of the century, but now only a few remain. Bishop's Oo – much larger and long-tailed – was thought extinct by the early 1900s, but then rediscovered on Maui in 1981: its being overlooked for so long is perhaps understandable because it lives in the upper levels of the rainforest canopy, with only its 'oh-oh' call to give it away.

The Hawaiian Crow (**103**) and the Marianas Crow, which is confined to Guam and Rota, are 'Endangered' and still declining. The Pink-billed Parrotfinch, endemic to Viti Levu in Fiji, may be at risk from destruction of its mature forest, but it is not as rare as was once thought: dark green with blue crown and red rump, this is one of several small grassfinches related to the Gouldian Finch of Australia, most of which are Indomalayan extending to the New Guinea area.

Thus, there is much to be worried about in the Pacific region and, if many of the most critically endangered species seem to be mainly in the Hawaiian Islands and Guam, perhaps this is because the birds of some other archipelagos are less well recorded. It may already be too late for several of the species mentioned. It is just possible, however, that, like Bishop's Oo, one or two 'extinct' birds remain to be rediscovered.

103
HAWAIIAN CROW
Corvus tropicus

The 40-odd typical crows – mostly blackish but some partly white, grey or brown – are found over much of the world except South America. This one is medium-large and dark sooty with paler wing-tips and a strong pointed bill; it is not remarkable except that it is endemic to Hawaii itself and, formerly abundant, is now on the verge of extinction. The largest population – under 10 – lives on the higher slopes of Mauna Loa; elsewhere only scattered pairs are left. Many crows do well in Man's environment, but this is a shy fruit-eating bird of wet forest and scrub; habitat degradation, illegal shooting, introduced rats and mosquito-borne diseases may all have contributed to its decline.

Antarctica and islands south of the Antarctic Convergence

Antarctic simply means 'opposite to Arctic', but the two are very different. The Arctic is a northern extension of North America and Eurasia: largely an almost land-locked ocean two-thirds covered by pack ice, it otherwise comprises Greenland, various small circumpolar islands, and those parts of Alaska, Canada and Siberia that lie beyond the tree limit.

In contrast, Antarctica is the fifth largest continent, half as big again as Australia and a quarter larger than Europe; at over 2000 m above sea-level, its average height is twice that of Asia, the second highest. The 13·3 million square km of land are shaped something like an apple with, near the 'stalk' formed by the Antarctic Peninsula, two bites out of opposite sides. The overlying frozen sheet, many metres thick, is said to account for nine-tenths of all the world's ice; and shelves of ice greatly diminish the vast bays that are the 'bites'. Mountains near the coast include the Vinson Massif, highest of all at 5140 m, but the continent is also divided into unequal parts by a 3000-km ridge with peaks up to 4500 m.

Antarctica is one of the coldest, windiest, most spectacular and least spoilt places on earth. Mean temperatures in August, before the sun reappears, vary on the coast from $-20°$ to $-30°$C, and inland from $-40°$ to $-70°$C (the record is $-89·2°$C). Even in midsummer the mean on the coast is mostly no higher than 0°C, except on the northern Antarctic Peninsula where it may reach as high as 15°C. Only a few thousand square kilometres of coastal land are ever exposed, even in summer; much of that is just rock, shingle and bare soil, but mosses and lichens appear on the warmer peninsula. These temperatures are made far worse by the wind chill of relentless westerlies roaring clockwise around the continent: the mean speed is 70 kph, with gusts up to 250 kph.

Included in the region are the oceans and small islands that lie south of the Antarctic Convergence, the boundary where the cold north-flowing polar surface waters meet and sink below those of the subantarctic zone already warmed by mixing with subtropical seas: this line varies between about 58°S and 48°S. South Shetland, South Orkney, South Georgia, South Sandwich, Bouvetøy, Heard and Macdonald are all Antarctic; Kerguelen and Macquarie, lying on or fractionally north of the boundary, are also included here.

Though the landmass is among the most inhospitable in the world, the adjacent seas are enormously rich because of the upwelling layer of warm deep water south of the Antarctic Convergence. This rises near the edge of Antarctica, bringing with it abundant nutrients that sustain vast shoals of shrimp-like krill and, in turn, the huge numbers of fishes and squids that eat them. All these are foods for the birds and marine mammals.

The birds

Antarctica is often envisaged as plastered with penguins, albatrosses and other colonial seabirds. In fact, most is uninhabitable. Nesting birds are confined to parts of the coastline and, importantly, to the 'apple stalk' of the warmer Antarctic Peninsula which, with its associated islands – South Shetland, South Orkney and many small islets along its west coast – extends north almost to 60°S.

The whole region, including all the islands within or on the line of the Antarctic Convergence, has 46 indigenous breeding species, representing 14 families (none of which is endemic), and four others which have either been introduced or have colonised as a result of introductions elsewhere. Most are seabirds, but totals of four ducks and four landbirds breed on certain islands, notably South Georgia, Kerguelen and Macquarie. Two of these have been introduced: the Mallard to Kerguelen, and New Zealand's Weka Rail to Macquarie. In addition, Common Starlings and Redpolls, naturalised by Man in New Zealand (*chapter 7*), have subsequently colonised Macquarie.

No birds have become extinct on the continent of Antarctica in historic times, though there are fossil remains of ancient species from long ice-free epochs before and after it broke away from Gondwanaland. Macquarie, however, has lost the Macquarie Rail (by 1894) and an endemic race of New Zealand's Red-fronted Parakeet (1911).

Of the breeding birds, only nine or ten are endemic as nesters to the region as a whole and only three to Antarctica proper. One of the latter, the South Polar Skua, ranges into and beyond the tropics when not nesting. The other two are more strictly endemic in that, apart from the odd wanderer, they remain inside the Antarctic Convergence throughout the year: these are the big Emperor Penguin, weighing up to 40 kg, and the largish Antarctic Petrel. The petrel is the one species that nests only along the cold continental coasts and not on the warmer peninsula.

Others of the region's endemic nesters that are in great numbers in this cold zone are Adélie Penguins and the all-white Snow Petrels. Both also extend to the oceanic islands of Antarctica, as do three of the last five birds restricted as breeders to the region: Chinstrap Penguins, Antarctic Fulmars and Snowy Sheathbills. The other two are the South Georgia Pipit and, endemic to Macquarie, the Royal Penguin.

All the birds so far, apart from the last two and the sheathbill, nest to some extent along the continental coasts but, in total, only 11 species breed in that cold zone: the first three penguins, the three petrels and the one skua mentioned, plus Southern Giant and Cape Petrels, Wilson's Storm-petrel and, in one area, the Antarctic race of the Broad-billed Prion. Southern Giant Petrels are bigger, if shorter-winged, than the smaller albatrosses and, like fulmars, they nest in the open and defend themselves by spitting oil. Wilson's Storm-petrels may be more familiar since they range well north in the world's three main oceans.

The warmer Antarctic Peninsula and its islands introduce a further six or seven species: very common are Gentoo and Macaroni Penguins; there are also Blue-eyed Cormorants, Antarctic Skuas, Kelp Gulls, Antarctic Terns and probably Black-bellied Storm-petrels. Thus, continental Antarctica's total of breeding species is a mere 17 or 18, including just five penguins (less than a third of the world's species), but some of the seabird colonies – rookeries in the case of penguins – are huge.

Apart from the Dark-mantled Sooty, which comes marginally into the region on Kerguelen, four albatrosses breed on the outer Antarctic islands. Wandering Albatrosses have the greatest wing-span of all existing birds, up to 3·5 m; Black-browed and Grey-headed are three-quarters as big; Light-mantled Sooties, like Dark-mantled, are smaller, with longer, pointed tails.

As well as the Royal Penguins on Macquarie, already mentioned, two more penguins come into the picture on these outer islands. King Penguins nest on South Georgia, Heard and Macquarie; and Rock-hoppers on the last two and Kerguelen. Both, like Gentoo and Macaroni Penguins, also breed on more subantarctic islands farther north.

Most of the petrel family, including fulmars, prions, gadfly-petrels and shearwaters, nest colonially in burrows or natural holes, but continental Antarctica's ground is generally unsuitable for burrowing. Thus, it is not surprising that all five petrels so far are fulmars and large species less vulnerable to predators. The outer islands of the region have richer soil, more vegetation and another 11 petrel species. Some 20 petrels, a third of the total, regularly feed in Antarctic waters.

Storm-petrels, a distinct family, nest colonially in scree and burrows. Scree boulders enable Wilson's Storm-petrels to breed on the Antarctic continent. There are certainly Black-bellied Storm-petrels on South Orkney, while they and Grey-backed both nest on South Georgia and other islands.

The dumpy and oddly auk-like diving-petrels, with rounded wings and whirring flight, are another distinct family. Both Georgian and Common Diving-petrels nest on South Georgia, Heard and Kerguelen. The only other additional seabirds of these outer islands are South Georgia and King Cormorants, and Lesser Sheathbills and Kerguelen Terns which both nest on Heard and Kerguelen.

Apart from the introduced Mallards on Kerguelen, the indigenous ducks of the region are Speckled Teals and Yellow-billed Pintails, both common in southern South America, which have isolated populations on South Georgia; and Pacific Black Ducks, widespread in Australasia and extending to Macquarie. The introduced Weka Rails, the self-assisted Common Starlings and Redpolls, and South Georgia's endemic pipit have already been mentioned. These are the only landbirds.

The relatively small island of South Georgia – actually 160 km long – might be described as the richest part of the region: it has 25 species (compared with 17 or 18 for continental Antarctica, three-and-a-half thousand times its size). Kerguelen is of similar area to South Georgia and has some 30 species, including the largest numbers of the possibly threatened Kerguelen Tern (*chapter* 5). Numbers of breeding species tend to increase as one goes north into warmer waters: the Crozet archipelago, for example, though much smaller in total area, has 35.

So what?

With a mere three species per million square km – a tiny figure compared with those of even the less bird-rich northern regions – what is all the fuss about? Why is the preservation of Antarctica so important when only three birds are endemic to the continent and only six more to the wider Antarctic region? There are no other land animals on Antarctica itself, apart from a few minute wingless insects; the only marine vertebrates are whales and seals, and about 100 species of fish. There are no flowering plants on the continent: just a sparse growth of mosses, lichens, fungi and algae on the islands and in the most favourable parts of the exposed coastal land.

Antarctica is a spectacular and almost unspoilt wilderness museum that offers unrivalled opportunities for undisturbed research; it is the only continent and one of the few really large areas of the world that can be described in those terms. The seas around are a hugely rich reserve of marine life whose loss or serious damage could have a knock-on effect world-wide.

The Antarctic Treaty of 1959 held all territorial claims in abeyance in the interest of international cooperation for scientific purposes. The new treaty signed in October 1991 by 23 consultative and eight observer nations will, when it comes into force in 1993, ban mining and oil-drilling for 50 years, as well as place tight restrictions on waste disposal and marine pollution; it will also protect indigenous plants and animals, and put essential limits on the tourism that can cause considerable damage through disturbance. The ban on mining – for long the most serious threat from certain quarters – can now be broken only with the approval of 75 per cent of the voting nations.

This book being concerned with threatened birds, it must suffice here to say that, if the Antarctic were seriously disturbed and developed, or became still more overfished, vast colonies of seabirds and marine mammals could be destroyed. The numbers of seabirds could be depleted dangerously. Worst hit would be Emperor, Adélie and Chinstrap Penguins – with Gentoos and Rockhoppers relying on populations elsewhere – as well as Antarctic Fulmars, Antarctic, Cape and Snow Petrels, Snowy Sheathbills, and South Polar Skuas. Now existing in vast numbers, several of those birds could quickly become endangered.

Will the world learn before it is too late?

FURTHER READING

Beehler, B.M., Pratt, T.K., and Zimmerman, D.A. (1986) *Birds of New Guinea*. Princeton UP.

Cade, T.J. (1982) *The Falcons of the World*. London: Collins.

Campbell, B., and Lack, E. (eds) (1985) *A Dictionary of Birds*. Calton: Poyser.

Collar, N.J., and Stuart, S.N. (1985) *Threatened Birds of Africa and Related Islands*. ICBP/IUCN Red Data Book, Pt 1, 3rd ed. Cambridge: ICBP.

Collar, N.J., and Andrew, P. (1988) *Birds to Watch: the ICBP World Checklist of Threatened Birds*. Cambridge: ICBP.

Darlington, P.J., Jr (1957) *Zoogeography*. New York.

Diamond, A.W. (ed) (1987) *Studies of Mascarene Island Birds*. Cambridge UP.

Fuller, E.R. (1987) *Extinct Birds*. London: Viking.

Greenway, J.C. (1967) *Extinct and Vanishing Birds of the World*. London: Dover.

Harrison, P. (1983) *Seabirds*. Beckenham: Croom Helm.

Hayman, P., Marchant, J., and Prater, T. (1986) *Shorebirds*. Beckenham: Croom Helm.

Howard, R., and Moore, A. (1991) *A Complete Checklist of the Birds of the World*. 2nd ed. London: Academic Press.

Inskipp, T. P. (1975) *All Heaven in a Rage* Sandy: RSPB.

Inskipp, T.P., and Thomas, G.J. (1976) *Airborne Birds*. Sandy: RSPB.

Inskipp, T., Broad, S., and Luxmoore, R. (1988) *Significant Trade in Wildlife: a Review of Selected Species in CITES Appendix II*. Cambridge: IUCN.

King, W. B. (1981) *Endangered Birds of the World: the ICBP Bird Red Data Book*. Washington, DC: Smithsonian/ICBP.

Lever, Sir C. (1987) *Naturalized Birds of the World*. London: Longman.

Long, J.L. (1981) *Introduced Birds of the World*. Newton Abbot: David & Charles.

Madge, S., and Burn, H. (1988) *Wildfowl*. Bromley: Christopher Helm.

Min. Ag. Fish. and Food (1989) *Importation of Birds: Mortality Statitics from Quarantine Returns, Year Ended 1988*. Colworth, Surrey: MAFF.

Mountfort, G., and Arlott, N. (1988) *Rare Birds of the World*. London: Collins.

Mullie, W. C., et al. (1989) *The Impact of Pesticides on Palearctic Migratory Birds in the Western Sahel*. Cambridge: ICBP.

Newton, I., and Chancellor, R.D. (eds) (1985) *Conservation Studies on Raptors*. Cambridge: ICBP.

Norton, J., Stuart, S.N., and Johnson, T. (1986) *World Checklist of Threatened Birds*. London: Nature Conservancy Council.

Pratt, H.D., Bruner, P.L. and Berrett, D.G. (1987) *The Birds of Hawaii and the Tropical Pacific*. Princeton UP.

Prestwich, A.A. (1955) *Records of Birds of Prey Bred in Captivity*. Private publ.

Sibley, C.G., and Monroe, B.L., Jr (1990) *Distribution and Taxonomy of Birds of the World*. New Haven/London: Yale UP.

Turner, A., and Rose, C. (1989) *Swallows and Martins*. Bromley: Christopher Helm.

White, C.M.N., and Bruce, M.D. (1986) *The Birds of Wallacea*. London: BOU.